MW00439838

Kiselev's
GEOMETRY

Book II. STEREOMETRY
by
A. P. Kiselev

Adapted from Russian
by Alexander Givental

Sumizdat

Published by Sumizdat
5426 Hillside Avenue, El Cerrito, California 94530, USA
http://www.sumizdat.org

University of California, Berkeley Cataloging-in-Publication Data
Kiselev, A. (Andrei Petrovich)
    Geometriia. Chast 2, Stereometriia. English
    Kiselev's Geometry. Book II, Stereometry / by A.P. Kiselev ;
adapted from Russian by Alexander Givental.
    El Cerrito, Calif. : Sumizdat, 2008.
    iv, 176 p. : ill. ; 23 cm.
    Includes bibliographical references and index.
    ISBN 978-0-9779852-1-0
    1. Geometry. 2. Geometry, Solid. I. Givental, Alexander.
QA453.K57313 2008

Library of Congress Control Number: 2008931141

Credits

Editing: Alisa Givental.

Consulting: Thomas Rike, Math Department, Oakland High School.

Linguistic advice: Ralph Raimi,
Department of Mathematics, The University of Rochester.

Front cover features art photography ⓒ by Svetlana Tretyakova.

Art advising: Irina Mukhacheva, http://irinartstudio.com

Copyright advising: Ivan Rothman, attorney-at-law.

Cataloging-in-publication: Catherine Moreno,
Technical Services Department, Library, UC Berkeley.

Layout, typesetting and graphics: using L^AT_EX and $Xfig$.

Printing and binding: *Thomson-Shore, Inc.*, http://www.tshore.com
Member of the Green Press Initiative.
7300 West Joy Road, Dexter, Michigan 48130-9701, USA.
Offset printing on 30% recycled paper; cover: by 4-color process on Kivar-7.

ISBN 978-0-9779852-1-0

Contents

* * *

The present volume completes the English adaptation of *Kiselev's Geometry*. The first volume, *Planimetry*, was published as [4] (see section Bibliography) and will be referred to as *Book I*. The reader is directed to Translator's Foreword in Book I for background information on the original work [5, 6]. Preparing Book II, I added about 250 exercises, expanded the sections on Similarity of polyhedra, Symmetries of space figures and Regular polyhedra, and wrote a new, last chapter. It contains a geometric approach to vectors, followed by a vector approach to logical foundations of geometry, and concludes with a constructive introduction into non-Euclidean plane geometry. While some accounts of such topics are certainly expected of every modern course in elementary geometry, any specific choices may have non-obvious mathematical and pedagogical implications. Some of them are explained in Translator's Afterword *Three controversies about mathematics, geometry, and education.*

Alexander Givental
Department of Mathematics
University of California Berkeley
July, 2008

Authors cited in this book:

Plato	*427 – 347 B.C.*
Euclid of Alexandria	*about 325 – 265 B.C.*
Archimedes of Syracuse	*287 – 212 B.C.*
Menelaus of Alexandria	*about 70 – 140 A.D.*
Pappus of Alexandria	*about 290 – 350 A.D.*
Johannes Kepler	*1571 – 1630*
Gérard Desargues	*1591 – 1661*
Bonaventura Cavalieri	*1598 – 1647*
Giovanni Ceva	*1647 – 1734*
Augustin Louis Cauchy	*1789 – 1857*
Nikolai Lobachevsky	*1792 – 1856*
János Bolyai	*1802 – 1860*
Arthur Cayley	*1821 – 1895*
Bernhard Riemann	*1826 – 1866*
Eugeneo Beltrami	*1835 – 1899*
Hermann Schwarz	*1843 – 1921*
Georg Cantor	*1845 – 1918*
Felix Klein	*1849 – 1925*
David Hilbert	*1862 – 1943*
Hermann Minkowski	*1864 – 1909*
Max Dehn	*1878 – 1952*
Albert Einstein	*1879 – 1955*
Hermann Weyl	*1885 – 1955*

Chapter 1

LINES AND PLANES

1 Drawing a plane

1. Preliminary remarks. In **stereometry** (called also **solid geometry**) one studies geometric figures not all of whose elements fit the same plane.

Geometric figures in space are shown on the plane of a diagram following certain conventions, intended to make the figures and their diagrams appear alike.

Many real objects around us have surfaces which resemble geometric planes and are shaped like rectangles: the cover of a book, a window pane, the surface of a desk, etc. When seen at an angle and from a distance, such surfaces appear to have the shape of a parallelogram. It is customary, therefore, to show a plane in a diagram as a parallelogram. The plane is usually denoted by one letter, e.g. "the plane M" (Figure 1).

Figure 1

2. Basic properties of the plane. Let us point out the following properties of planes, which are accepted without proof, i.e. considered axioms.

1

(1) *If two points[1] of a line lie in a given plane, then every point of the line lies in this plane.*

(2) *If two planes have a common point, then they intersect in a line passing through this point.*

(3) *Through every three points not lying on the same line, one can draw a plane, and such a plane is unique.*

3. Corollaries. (1) *Through a line and a point outside it, one can draw a plane, and such a plane is unique.* Indeed, the point together with any two points on the line form three points not lying on the same line, through which a plane can therefore be drawn, and such a plane is unique.

(2) *Through two intersecting lines, one can draw a plane, and such a plane is unique.* Indeed, taking the intersection point and one more point on each of the lines, we obtain three points through which a plane can be drawn, and such a plane is unique.

(3) *Through two parallel lines, one can draw only one plane.* Indeed, parallel lines, by definition, lie in the same plane. Such a plane is unique, since through one of the lines and any point of the other line, at most one plane can be drawn.

4. Rotating a plane about a line. *Through each line in space, infinitely many planes can be drawn.*

Indeed, let a line a be given (Figure 2). Take any point A outside it. Through the line a and the point A, a unique plane is passing (§3). Let us call this plane M. Take a new point B outside the plane M. Through the line a and the point B, too, a unique plane is passing. Let us call this plane N. It cannot coincide with M, since it contains the point B which does not lie in the plane M. Furthermore, we can take in space yet another point C outside the planes M and N. Through the line a and the point C, yet a new plane is passing. Denote it P. It coincides neither with M nor with N, since it contains the point C which lies neither in the plane M nor in the plane N. Proceeding by taking more and more points in space, we will thus obtain more and more planes passing through the given line a. There will be *infinitely many* such planes. All these planes can be considered as various positions of the same plane which *rotates* about the line a.

We may therefore formulate one more property of the plane: *a plane can be rotated about every line lying in this plane.*

---

[1] As in Book I, we will always assume that expressions like "three points," "two planes," etc. refer to *distinct* points, planes, etc.

EXERCISES

1. Explain why three-legged stools standing on flat floor are always stable, while many four-legged ones totter.

2. Using the axioms from §2, show that the plane described in the proof of Corollary 1 of §3 contains, indeed, the given line and the given point as required. Similarly, complete the proofs of Corollaries 2 and 3.

3. Prove that through any two points in space infinitely many planes can be drawn.

4. Prove that if through three given points two planes can be drawn, then infinitely many planes through these points can be drawn.

5.⋆ Prove that several lines in space, intersecting pairwise, either lie in the same plane or pass through the same point.

2 Parallel lines and planes

5. Skew lines. Two lines can be positioned in space in such a way that no plane can be drawn through them. For example, take two lines AB and DE (Figure 3), of which the first one lies in a certain plane P, and the second one intersects this plane at a point C, which does not lie on the first line. No plane can be drawn through these two lines, since otherwise there would exist two planes passing through the line AB and the point C: one (P) intersecting the line DE and the other one containing it, which is impossible (§3).

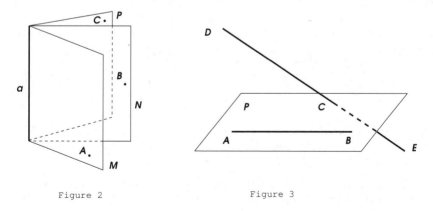

Figure 2   Figure 3

Of course, two lines not lying in the same plane do not intersect each other no matter how far they are extended. However they are not called parallel, the term being reserved for those lines which, *being in the same plane*, do not intersect each other no matter how far they are extended.

Two lines not lying in the same plane are called **skew lines**.

6. A line and a plane parallel to each other. A plane and a line not lying in this plane are called **parallel** if they do not intersect each other no matter how far they are extended.

7. Theorem. *If a given line* (*AB*, Figure 4) *does not lie in a given plane* (*P*) *but is parallel to a line* (*CD*) *that lies in it, then the given line is parallel to the plane.*

Through *AB* and *CD*, draw the plane *R* and assume that the line *AB* intersects the plane *P*. Then the intersection point, being a point of the line *AB*, lies in the plane *R* that contains *AB*, and at the same time it lies in the plane *P*, of course. Then the intersection point, being in both planes *R* and *P*, must lie on the line *CD* of intersection of these two planes. But this is impossible, since *AB*∥*CD* by the hypothesis. Thus the assumption that the line *AB* intersects the plane *P* is false, and hence *AB*∥*P*.

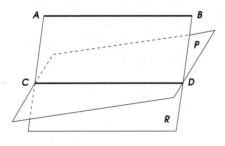

Figure 4

8. Theorem. *If a given line* (*AB*, Figure 4) *is parallel to a given plane* (*P*), *then it is parallel to the intersection line* (*CD*) *of the given plane with every plane* (*R*) *containing the given line.*

Indeed, firstly the lines *AB* and *CD* lie in the same plane, and secondly they cannot intersect each other, since otherwise the line *AB* would intersect the plane *P*, which is impossible.

9. Corollary. *If a line* (*AB*, Figure 5) *is parallel to each of two intersecting planes* (*P* and *Q*), *then it is parallel to their intersection line* (*CD*).

Draw a plane through *AB* and any point *C* of the line *CD*. This plane must intersect each of the planes *P* and *Q* along a line parallel to AB (§8) and passing through the point C. But according to the parallel postulate (Book I, §75), through a given point, there is only one line parallel to a given line. Therefore the lines of intersection must be the same line. It lies in each of the planes P and Q and thus coincides with the line CD of their intersection. Hence $CD\|AB$.

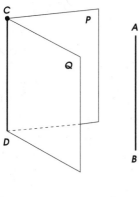

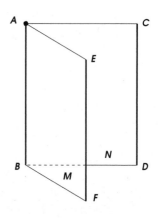

Figure 5   Figure 6

10. Corollary. *If two lines* (AB *and* CD, *Figure 6*) *are parallel to a third one* (EF), *then they are parallel to each other.*

If the three lines lie in the same plane, then the required conclusion follows immediately from the parallel postulate. Let us assume, therefore, that the three lines do not lie in the same plane.

Draw the plane M through the line EF and the point A, and the plane N through the line CD and the point A. Since the lines CD and EF are parallel, each of them is parallel to the intersection line of these planes (§8). Since through the point A, there is only one line parallel to EF, the intersection line of the planes M and N is AB. Thus $CD\|AB$.

11. Parallel planes. Two planes are called **parallel**, if they do not intersect each other no matter how far they are extended.

12. Theorem. *If two intersecting lines* (AB *and* AC, *Figure 7*) *of one plane* (P) *are respectively parallel to two lines* ($A'B'$ *and* $A'C'$) *of another plane* (P'), *then these planes are parallel.*

The lines AB and AC are parallel to the plane P' (§7).

Suppose that the planes P and P' intersect along a certain line DE (Figure 7). Then $AB\|DE$ and $AC\|DE$ (§8).

Thus, the plane P contains two lines AB and AC passing through A and parallel to the same line DE, which is impossible. Hence the planes P and P' do not intersect each other.

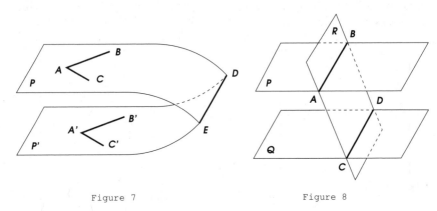

Figure 7   Figure 8

13. Theorem. *If two parallel planes* (P *and* Q, Figure 8) *are intersected by a third plane* (R), *then the intersection lines* (AB *and* CD) *are parallel.*

Firstly, the lines AB and CD lie in the same plane (R). Secondly, they cannot intersect, since otherwise the planes P and Q would intersect each other, thereby contradicting the hypothesis.

14. Theorem. *The segments* (AC *and* BD, Figure 9), *cut off by parallel planes* (P *and* Q) *on parallel lines, are congruent.*

Draw the plane containing the parallel lines AC and BD. It intersects the planes P and Q along the parallel lines AB and CD respectively. Therefore the quadrilateral $ABDC$ is a parallelogram, and hence $AC = BD$.

15. Theorem. *Two angles* (BAC *and* $B'A'C'$, Figure 10) *whose respective sides are parallel and have the same direction, are congruent and lie either in parallel planes* (P *and* P') *or in the same plane.*

When two angles with respectively parallel and similarly directed sides lie in the same plane, their congruence has been established in Book I, §79. Let us assume that the planes P and P' do not coincide. Then they are parallel, as has been shown in §12.

To prove that the angles in question are congruent, mark on their sides arbitrary but respectively congruent segments $AB = A'B'$ and $AC = A'C'$, and draw the lines AA', BB', CC', BC and $B'C'$. Since the segments AB and $A'B'$ are congruent and parallel (and have the same direction), the figure $ABB'A'$ is a parallelogram. Therefore AA' and BB' are congruent and parallel. For the same reason, AA' and CC' are congruent and parallel. Therefore $BB'\|CC'$ (§10) and $BB' = CC'$, i.e. $BCC'B'$ is a parallelogram. Thus $BC = B'C'$, and hence $\triangle ABC = \triangle A'B'C'$ (by the SSS-test). Therefore $\angle A = \angle A'$.

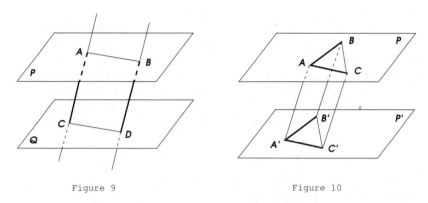

Figure 9   Figure 10

16. Problem. *Through a given point* $(M,$ *Figure 11), not lying on either of two given skew lines* $(a$ *and* $b)$, *find a line intersecting each of the given ones.*

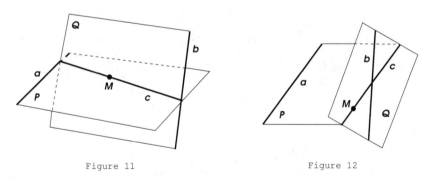

Figure 11   Figure 12

Solution. The line in question must pass through the point M and intersect the line a, and therefore it has to lie in the plane P passing through M and a (since two of its points lie in this plane: M, and the intersection point with a). Similarly, the line in question has to lie in the plane Q passing through M and b. Thus this line has to coincide with the intersection line c of the planes P and Q. If this intersection line is parallel to neither a nor b, then it will intersect each of them (since it lies in the same plane with either of them: a

and c lie in the plane P, and b and c lie in the plane Q). Then the line c will intersect a and b and pass through M, and will therefore provide the unique solution of the problem. If however $c\|a$ (Figure 12) or $c\|b$, then the problem has no solution.

17. Remark. There is some resemblance between the above problem, and the problems of constructing plane figures using drafting devices such as straightedge and compass. For purposes of describing figures in space, the drafting devices become useless. Consequently, in solid geometry we will refrain from formulating construction problems. However the question of *finding* a geometric figure satisfying a certain set of requirements can be understood the same way as it has been done in the above solution. Namely, one can seek to find out if the required figure *exists*, and if it is *unique* (or, more generally, how many solutions there are, and how the number of solutions depends on the given data).

18. Problem. *Through a given point* (A, Figure 13) *not lying in a given plane* (P), *find a plane parallel to the given one.*

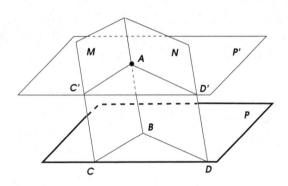

Figure 13

Solution. On the plane P, draw an arbitrary pair of intersecting lines BC and BD. Draw two auxiliary planes: M through the point A and the line BC, and N through the point A and the line BD. Every plane parallel to P and passing through A must intersect the plane M along the line AC' parallel to BC, and the plane N along the line AD' parallel to BD (§13). There is a unique plane P' containing the lines AC' and AD', and this plane is parallel to P (§12). Thus the solution exists and is unique.

Corollary. *Through each point not lying on a given plane, there exists a unique plane parallel to the given one.*

EXERCISES

6. Prove that through every point in space, not lying on a given line, there exists a unique line parallel to the given one.

7. Derive from the parallel postulate that, in a plane, two lines parallel to a third one are parallel to each other.

8. Prove that two planes parallel to a third one are parallel to each other.

9. Prove that all lines parallel to a given plane and passing through the same point lie in the same plane parallel to the given one.

10. Prove that two parallel lines, lying respectively in two intersecting planes, are parallel to the intersection line of these planes.

11. Can two planes intersect, if the first plane contains two lines respectively parallel to two lines contained in the second plane?

12. Prove that if a line a is parallel to a plane M, then every line parallel to a and passing through a point of M lies in M.

13. Prove that for every pair of skew lines a and b, there is a unique pair of planes: one passing through a and parallel to b, the other passing through b and parallel to a, and that these planes are parallel.

14. Given a pair of skew lines a and b, find the geometric locus of points M for which there is no line passing through M and intersecting a and b.

15. Find a plane passing through a given point and parallel to two given lines.

16. Find a line intersecting two given lines and parallel to a third one.

17. Find the geometric locus of midpoints of segments connecting a given point with points lying on a given plane.

18. Let AB and CD be skew lines. Prove that the midpoints of the segments AC, AD, BC, and BD are vertices of a parallelogram, and that its plane is parallel to the lines AB and CD.

19.[⋆] Compute the ratios in which the plane passing through barycenters of the triangles ABC, ACD, and ADB, not lying in the same plane, divides the sides AB, AC, and AD.

3   Perpendiculars and slants

19. A line perpendicular to lines in a plane. In order to understand which lines should be considered perpendicular to a given plane, let us prove the following proposition.

Theorem. *If a given line* (*AO*, Figure 14) *intersecting a given plane* (*M*) *is perpendicular to two lines* (*OB* and *OC*) *drawn in the plane through its intersection point* (*O*) *with the given line, then the given line is perpendicular to any other line* (*OD*) *drawn in the plane through the same intersection point.*

On the extension of the line *AO*, mark the segments *OA'* congruent to *AO*. On the plane *M*, draw any line intersecting the three lines, drawn from the point *O*, at some points *B*, *D*, and *C*. Connect these points with *A* and *A'* by straight segments. We thus obtain several triangles, which we examine in the following order.

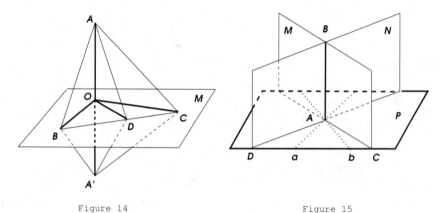

Figure 14   Figure 15

First, consider the triangles *ABC* and *A'BC*. They are congruent, since *BC* is their common side, *BA = BA'* as two slants to the line *AA'* whose feet are the same distance away from the foot *O* of the perpendicular *BO* (Book I, §52), and *CA = CA'* — for the same reason. It follows from the congruence of these triangles, that ∠*ABC* = ∠*A'BC*.

Next, consider the triangles *ADB* and *A'DB*. They are congruent, since *BD* is their common side, *BA = BA'*, and ∠*ABD* = ∠*A'BD*. It follows from the congruence of these triangles, that *DA = DA'*.

Finally, consider the triangle *ADA'*. It is isosceles, and therefore its median *DO* is perpendicular to the base *AA'*.

20. Definition. A line is called **perpendicular** to a plane if it intersects the plane and forms a right angle with every line lying in the plane and passing through the intersection point. In this case, one would also say that the plane is perpendicular to the line.

The previous theorem shows that a given line is perpendicular to a plane whenever it is perpendicular to two lines lying in the plane and passing through its intersection point with the given line.

A line intersecting a plane, but not perpendicular to it, is called **oblique** to this plane, or a **slant**.

The intersection point of a line with a plane is called the **foot** of the perpendicular or of the slant.

21. Theorem. *Through every point* (A, Figure 15) *lying on a given line* (AB), *a plane perpendicular to the line can be drawn, and such a plane is unique.*

Draw any two planes M and N through the line AB, and at the point A, erect perpendiculars to AB inside these planes: AC in the plane M, and AD in the plane N. The plane P, passing through the lines AC and AD, is perpendicular to AB. Conversely, every plane perpendicular to AB at the point A must intersect M and N along lines perpendicular to AB, i.e. along AC and AD respectively. Therefore every plane perpendicular to AB at A coincides with P.

22. Corollary. *All lines perpendicular to a given line* (AB, Figure 15) *at a given point* (A) *lie in the same plane, namely the plane* (P) *perpendicular to the given line at the given point.*

Indeed, the plane passing through any *two* lines perpendicular to AB at A is perpendicular to AB at the point A and therefore coincides with the plane P.

23. Corollary. *Through every point* (C, Figure 15) *not lying on a given line* (AB), *one can draw a plane perpendicular to the given line, and such a plane is unique.*

Draw an auxiliary plane M through C and the line AB, and drop from C the perpendicular CA to AB inside the plane M. Every plane perpendicular to AB and passing through C must intersect the plane M along a line perpendicular to AB, i.e. along the line CA. Therefore such a plane must coincide with the plane P passing through the point A and perpendicular to the line AB.

24. Corollary. *At every point* (A, Figure 15) *of a given plane* (P), *a perpendicular line* (AB) *can be erected, and such a line is unique.*

In the plane P, draw two arbitrary lines a and b passing through A. Every line perpendicular to P at the point A will be perpendicular to each a and b, and therefore will lie in the plane M perpendicular to a at A, and in the plane N perpendicular to b at A. Thus it will coincide with the intersection line AB of the planes M and N.

25. Comparing the perpendicular and slants.[2] When from the same point A (Figure 16), a perpendicular AB and a slant AC to the same plane P not passing through A are drawn, the segment BC, connecting the feet of the perpendicular and the slant is called the **projection** of the slant to the plane P. Thus the segment BC is the projection of the slant AC, the segment BD is the projection of the slant AD, etc.

26. Theorem. *If from the same point* $(A,$ *Figure 16)* **not** *lying in the given plane* (P), *a perpendicular* (AB), *and any slants* $(AC, AD, AE, \dots)$ *to this plane are drawn, then:*

(1) *slants with congruent projections are congruent;*

(2) *the slant with the greater projection is greater.*

Indeed, rotating the right triangles ABC and ABD around the leg AB, we can superimpose their planes with the plane of the triangle ABE. Then all the perpendicular AB and all the slants will fall into the same plane, and all their projections will lie in the same line. Then the conclusions of the theorem follow from the corresponding results in plane geometry (Book I, §52).

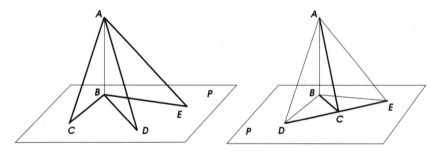

Figure 16   Figure 17

Remark. Each of the slants AC, AD, AE is the hypotenuse of a right triangle, of which AB is a leg, and hence the slants are greater than the perpendicular AB. We conclude that the *perpendicular dropped from a point to a plane* (see §35) *is the shortest of all segments connecting this point with any point of the plane.* Consequently, the length of the perpendicular is taken for the measure of the **distance** from the point to the plane.

---

[2]For the sake of brevity, the terms "perpendicular" and "slant" are often used instead of "the segment of the perpendicular between its foot and the given point," and "the segment of the slant between its foot and the given point."

27. Converse theorems. *If from a point not lying in a given plane, a perpendicular and any slants are drawn, then:*

(1) *congruent slants have congruent projections;*

(2) *greater slants have greater projections.*

We leave the proof (by *reductio ad absurdum*) to the reader.

28. The theorem of the three perpendiculars. The following theorem will prove useful later on.

Theorem. *The line* $(DE$, Figure 17) *drawn in a plane* (P) *through the foot of a slant* (AC) *and perpendicular to its projection* (BC), *is perpendicular to the slant itself.*

On the line DE, mark arbitrary but congruent segments CD and CE, and connect each of the points A and B with D and E by straight segments. Then we have: $BD = BE$ (since B lies on the perpendicular bisector BC of the segment DE in the plane P), and consequently $AD = AE$ (as slants to the plane P with congruent projections BD and BE). The triangle DAE is therefore isosceles, and hence its median AC is perpendicular to the base DE.

This proposition is often called *the theorem of the three perpendiculars* because it relates the following three perpendicular pairs: $AB \perp P$, $BC \perp DE$, and $AC \perp DE$.

29. Converse theorem. *If a slant* $(AC$, Figure 17) *to a given plane* (P) *is perpendicular to a line* (DE) *passing through the foot of the slant and lying in the plane, then the line is perpendicular to the projection* (BC) *of the slant.*

Repeat the constructions performed in the proof of the direct theorem, i.e. mark arbitrary but congruent segments CD and DE on the line DE, and connect each of the points A and B with D and E. Then we have: $AD = AE$ (since A lies in the plane of $\triangle ADE$ on the perpendicular bisector of the segment DE), and consequently $BD = BE$ (as projections of congruent slants AD and AE). The $\triangle DBE$ is therefore isosceles, and hence its median BC is perpendicular to the base DE.

30. Relations between parallel and perpendicular lines and planes. There is a dependence between the properties of lines or planes to be parallel, and the property of a line and a plane to be perpendicular. Namely, if certain elements of a given figure are parallel, one may be able to conclude that certain other elements are perpendicular, and conversely, if certain elements are perpendicular, then certain other elements turn out to be parallel. This relation between parallel and perpendicular lines and planes is expressed by the theorems described below.

31. Theorem. *If a plane* $(P,$ Figure 18$)$ *is perpendicular to one of two given parallel lines* $(AB),$ *then it is perpendicular to the other* $(CD).$

In the plane $P,$ draw through the point B any two lines BE and $BF,$ and through the point D two lines DG and DH parallel to BE and BF respectively. Then we have: $\angle ABE = \angle CDG$ and $\angle ABF = \angle CDH$ as angles with respectively parallel sides. But $\angle ABE$ and $\angle ABF$ are right angles (since $AB \perp P$), and hence $\angle CDG$ and $\angle CDH$ are also right angles. Therefore $CD \perp P$ (§20).

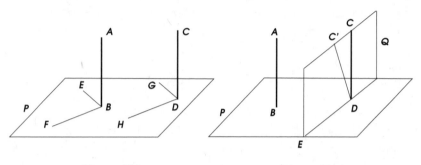

Figure 18　　　　　　　　　　　Figure 19

32. Converse theorem. *If two lines* $(AB$ and $CD,$ Figure 19$)$ *are perpendicular to the same plane* $(P),$ *then they are parallel.*

Let us assume the opposite, i.e. that the lines AB and CD are not parallel. Through the point $D,$ draw the line parallel to $AB;$ under our assumption, it will be a certain line DC' different from $DC.$ We have: $DC' \perp P$ by the direct theorem, and and $DC \perp P$ by the hypotheses. Therefore two perpendiculars to the plane P are erected at the same point $D,$ which is impossible by §24. Therefore our assumption was false, and hence the lines AB and CD are parallel.

33. Theorem. *If a line* $(AA',$ Figure 20$)$ *is perpendicular to one of two given parallel planes* $(P$ and $P'),$ *then it is perpendicular to the other.*

Through the line $AA',$ draw any two planes. Each of them intersects the planes P and P' along parallel lines: one along AB and $A'B',$ the other along AC and $A'C'.$ Since the line AA' is perpendicular to $P,$ it is perpendicular to the lines AB and $AC,$ and therefore it is also perpendicular to the lines $A'B'$ and $A'C'$ respectively parallel to them. Thus AA' is perpendicular to the plane P' passing through $A'B'$ and $A'C'.$

34. Converse theorem. *If two given planes* (P and Q, Figure 20) *are perpendicular to the same line* (AB), *then they are parallel.*

Otherwise, i.e. if the planes P and Q intersected, we would have two planes passing through a point of intersection and perpendicular to the same line, which is impossible (§23).

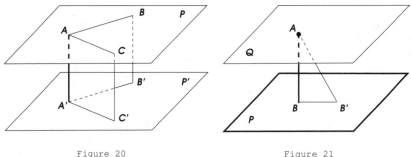

Figure 20   Figure 21

35. Corollary. *From a given point* (A, Figure 21), *not lying on a given plane* (P), *a perpendicular* (AB) *to this plane can be dropped, and such a perpendicular is unique.*

Through the given point A, draw the plane Q parallel to P (§18), and erect from A the perpendicular AB to Q (§24). According to §33, the line AB is perpendicular to P. The uniqueness of such a perpendicular is obvious, since otherwise, i.e. if another perpendicular AB' (Figure 21) were dropped from A to P, we would have a triangle ABB' with two right angles B and B', which is impossible.

Remark. Combining this Corollary with results of §§21, 23, and 24, we see that: *through a point (lying or not on a given plane), there is a unique line perpendicular to this plane,* and *through a point (lying or not on a given line), there is a unique plane perpendicular to this line.*

EXERCISES

20. Prove that there is a unique line in space, perpendicular to a given line and passing through a given point not lying on it.

21. Prove that there are infinitely many lines in space perpendicular to a given line and passing through a given point on it.

22. Prove that all points of a line parallel to a given plane are equidistant from the plane.

23. Prove that all points of one of two parallel planes are equidistant from the other.

24. Prove that if a plane and a line are perpendicular to the same line, then they are parallel to each other.

25. Prove that if a line a parallel to a plane P intersects a line b perpendicular to P, then a is perpendicular to b.

26. Find a line perpendicular to two given skew lines.

27. Prove that if a point A is equidistant from B, C, and D, then the projection of A to the plane BCD is the circumcenter of $\triangle BCD$.

28. Find the geometric locus of points equidistant from: (a) two given points, (b) three given non-collinear points.

4   Dihedral and some other angles

36. Dihedral angles. A plane is divided by a line lying in it into two parts, called **half-planes**, and the line is called the **edge** of each of these half-planes. A figure in space formed by two half-planes (P and Q, Figure 22) which have the same edge (AB) is called a **dihedral angle**. The line AB is called the **edge** and the half-planes P and Q **faces** of the dihedral angle. Space is divided by the faces into two parts, called the **interior**, and **exterior** of the dihedral angle (and defined similarly to how it was done in Book I, §13 for angles in plane geometry).

A dihedral angle is usually denoted by the two letters marking the edge (e.g. a dihedral angle AB). If several dihedral angles in a diagram have the same edge, then we will denote each of them by four letters, of which the middle two mark the edge, and the outer two mark the faces (e.g. a dihedral angle $SCDR$, Figure 23).

If from an arbitrary point D on the edge AB of a dihedral angle (Figure 24), a ray perpendicular to the edge is drawn in each face, then the angle CDE formed by these two rays is called a **linear angle** of the dihedral angle.

The measure of the linear angle of a dihedral angle does not depend on the position of its vertex on the edge. Namely, the linear angles CDE and $C'D'E'$ are congruent, because their sides are respectively parallel and have the same direction.

The plane containing a linear angle of a dihedral angle is perpendicular to the edge since it contains two lines perpendicular to it. Thus, linear angles of a dihedral angle are obtained by intersecting both faces by planes perpendicular to the edge.

37. Congruence and comparison of dihedral angles.

Two dihedral angles are **congruent** if they become superimposed when one of them is embedded into the interior of the other, so that their edges coincide; otherwise, the one of them that will lie inside the other is considered **smaller**.

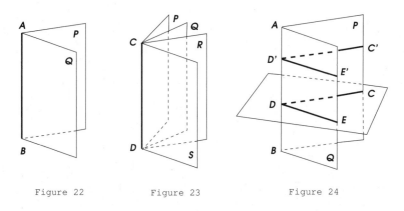

Figure 22   Figure 23   Figure 24

Similarly to angles in plane geometry, dihedral angles can be **vertical**, **supplementary**, etc.

If two supplementary dihedral angles are congruent to each other, then each of them is called a **right dihedral angle**.

Theorems. (1) *Congruent dihedral angles have congruent linear angles.*

(2) *The greater of two dihedral angles has the greater linear angle.*

Let $PABQ$ and $P'A'B'Q'$ (Figure 25) be two dihedral angles. Embed the angle $A'B'$ into the angle AB so that the edge $A'B'$ coincides with the edge AB, and the face P' with the face P. Then, if these dihedral angles are congruent, the face Q' will coincide with the face Q. However, if the angle $A'B'$ is smaller, the face Q' will occupy a certain position Q'' in the interior of the dihedral angle AB.

Having noticed this, pick on the common edge any point B, and through this point draw the plane R perpendicular to the edge. Intersecting this plane with the faces of the dihedral angles, we obtain their linear angles. Clearly, if the dihedral angles coincide, then their linear angles will turn out to be the same angle CBD. If the dihedral angles do not coincide (i.e. the face Q' occupies the position Q''), then the greater dihedral angle will turn out to have the greater linear angle, namely $\angle CBD > \angle C''BD$.

38. Converse theorems. (1) *Congruent linear angles correspond to congruent dihedral angles.*

(2) *The greater of two linear angles corresponds to the greater dihedral angle.*

These theorems are easy to prove by *reductio ad absurdum.*

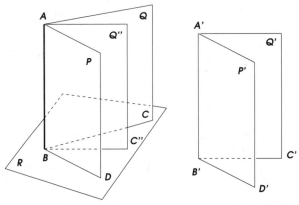

Figure 25

39. Corollaries. (1) *Right dihedral angles correspond to right linear angles, and vice versa.*

Let a dihedral angle $PABQ$ (Figure 26) be right. This means that it is congruent to its supplementary angle $P'ABQ$. But then the linear angles CDE and CDE' are also congruent, and since they are supplementary, each of them is right. Conversely, if the supplementary linear angles CDE and CDE' are congruent, then the corresponding dihedral angles are congruent, and therefore each of them is right.

(2) *All right dihedral angles are congruent* because they have congruent linear angles.

Similarly, one can easily prove that:

(3) *Vertical dihedral angles are congruent.*

(4) *Dihedral angles with respectively parallel and similarly (or oppositely) directed faces are congruent.*

(5) For the measure of a dihedral angle, one takes the degree measure of its linear angle. Thus, *a dihedral angle containing n degrees is congruent to the sum of n **unit dihedral angles.***

Two intersecting planes form two pairs of vertical dihedral angles, supplementary to each other. The measure of the smaller of these dihedral angles is used to measure the **angle between two planes**.

40. Perpendicular planes. Two planes are called **perpendicular** if they intersect and form right dihedral angles.

Theorem (test for perpendicular planes). *If a plane* $(Q$, Figure 26) *contains a line* (CD) *perpendicular to another plane* (P), *then these two planes are perpendicular.*

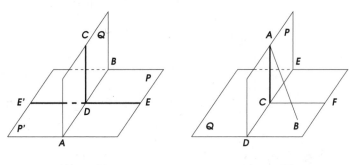

Figure 26   Figure 27

Let AB be the intersection line of the planes P and Q. On the plane P, draw $DE \perp AB$. Then $\angle CDE$ is the linear angle of the dihedral angle $PABQ$. Since the line CD is perpendicular to P by the hypothesis, it is perpendicular to DE. Thus the angle CDE is right, and therefore the dihedral angle is right, i.e. the plane Q is perpendicular to the plane P.

41. Theorem. *The perpendicular dropped from a point* $(A$, Figure 27) *of one of two given perpendicular planes* $(P$ and $Q)$, *to the other plane* (Q) *lies entirely in the first plane.*

Let AB be the perpendicular in question, and suppose that it does not lie in the plane P (as shown in Figure 27). Let DE be the intersection line of the planes P and Q. Draw on the plane P the line $AC \perp DE$, and on the plane Q the line $CF \perp DE$. Then the angle ACF will be right as the linear angle of a right dihedral angle. Therefore the line AC, being perpendicular to DE and CF, will be perpendicular to the plane Q. Thus we will have two perpendiculars dropped from the same point A to the plane Q, namely AB and AC. Since this is impossible (§35), our assumption had to be false, and therefore the perpendicular AB lies in the plane P.

42. Corollary. *The intersection line* $(AB$, Figure 28) *of two planes* $(P$ and $Q)$ *perpendicular to a third plane* (R) *is perpendicular to this plane.*

Indeed, if from any point A of the intersection line of the planes P and Q, we drop the perpendicular to the plane R, then this per-

pendicular will lie, according to the previous theorem, in each of the
planes P and Q, and therefore coincide with AB.

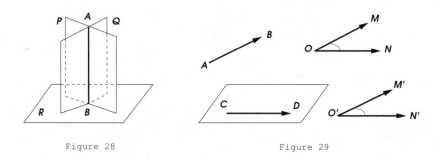

Figure 28   Figure 29

43. Angles between skew lines. Given positions and directions of two skew lines (AB and CD, Figure 29), the angle between
them is defined as any angle (MON) obtained by picking an arbitrary point O in space and drawing from it two rays (OM and ON)
respectively parallel to the skew lines (AB and CD) and similarly
directed to them.

The measure of this angle does not depend on the choice of the
point O, for if another such angle $M'O'N'$ is drawn, then $\angle MON =$
$\angle M'O'N'$ since these angles have respectively parallel and similarly
directed sides.

Now on, we use the terms **angle between lines** and **perpendicular lines** even if the lines do not meet.

44. Orthogonal projections. As we have discussed in §25,
when from a given point, the perpendicular and a slant to a given
plane are drawn, then the segment connecting the feet of the perpendicular and the slant is called the projection of the slant to the
plane. We now give a more general definition of **projection**.

(1) The **orthogonal** (or **Cartesian**) projection of a point to
a given plane (e.g. of the point M to the plane P in Figure 30)
is defined as the foot (M') of the perpendicular dropped from this
point to the plane.

For the sake of brevity we will usually omit the adjective "orthogonal" and say simply "projection."

(2) The **projection of a given figure** (e.g. a curve) to a given
plane is defined as the geometric locus of projections of all points of
this figure.

In particular, if the curve being projected is a straight line (*AB*, Figure 30) not perpendicular to the plane (*P*), then its projection to this plane is also a line. Indeed, if through the line *AB* and the perpendicular *MM'* dropped to the plane from a point *M* of the line, the plane *Q* is drawn, then this plane will be perpendicular to the plane *P*. Therefore the perpendicular dropped to the plane *P* from any point of the line *AB* (e.g. from the point *N*) will lie in the plane *Q* (§41). Thus projections of all points of the line *AB* will lie in the intersection line (*A'B'*) of the planes *P* and *Q*. Conversely, every point of the line *A'B'* is the projection of some point of the line *AB*, because the perpendicular to the plane *P* erected at any point of the line *A'B'* will lie in the plane *Q* and therefore intersect the line *AB* at some point. Thus the line *A'B'*, is the geometric locus of projections of all points of the line *AB*, i.e. it is the projection of the line.

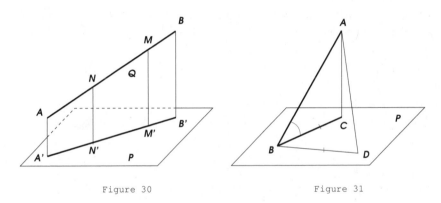

Figure 30   Figure 31

45. The angle a slant makes with a plane. Given a line (*AB*, Figure 31), oblique to a given plane (*P*), the angle between them is defined as the acute angle (*ABC*) formed by this line with its projection to the plane. This angle has the property of being the least of all angles which the given slant *AB* forms with lines drawn in the plane *P* through the foot *B* of the slant. Let us prove, for example, that the angle *ABC* is smaller than the angle *ABD* shown in Figure 31. For this, we mark the segment *BD* = *BC* and connect *D* with *A*. The triangles *ABC* and *ABD* have two pairs of respectively congruent sides, but their third sides are not congruent, namely: *AC* < *AD*, since the perpendicular to a plane is shorter than any slant dropped from the same point (§26). Therefore ∠*ABC* < ∠*ABD* (Book I, §50).

EXERCISES

29. Provide proofs of the theorems stated in §38.

30. Prove Corollary 3 in §39: Vertical dihedral angles are congruent.

31. Prove that a plane and a line both making right angles with another line are parallel to each other.

32. Prove that a line parallel to a given plane makes a right angle to any line perpendicular to the plane.

33. Prove that in an acute dihedral angle, the sides of any linear angle are projections of each other to the faces of the angle.

34. Find a plane containing a given line and perpendicular to a given plane.

35. Given a plane P and a line $a \| P$, find a plane containing the line a and making a given angle with the plane P.

36. Given a plane P and two points A and B on the same side of it, find a point C on the plane P such that the sum $AC + BC$ is minimal.

37. Find the greatest among the dihedral angles between a given plane and all planes containing a given slant to it.

38. Prove that if the intersection points of a line with faces of a dihedral angle are the same distance away from the edge, then the angles between the line and the faces are congruent.

39. Can four lines in space (not necessarily passing through the same point) be pairwise perpendicular?

40. Prove that the degree measures of angles formed by a given line with a line and a plane perpendicular to each other add up to 90°.

41. Prove that the projection of a parallelogram to a plane is a parallelogram.

42. Prove that the projection to a given plane of the barycenter of a given triangle coincides with the barycenter of the projection of the triangle.

43.[*] In space, four points A, B, C, and D are given such that $AB = AC$ and $DB = DC$. Prove that the lines AD and BC are perpendicular.

44.[*] Prove that a line making congruent angles with three pairwise intersecting lines of a plane, is perpendicular to the plane.

45.[*] Compute the angle between a line and a plane if the line forms the angles of 45° and 60° with two perpendicular lines lying in the plane.

5 Polyhedral angles

46. Definitions. Take several angles (Figure 32): ASB, BSC, CSD, ..., ESF, which being consecutively adjacent to each other, lie in the same plane around a common vertex S. Rotate the plane of the angle ASB about the side SB (common with the angle BSC) so that it forms some dihedral angle with the plane BSC. Then, keeping the dihedral angle unchanged, rotate it about the line SC so that the plane BSC forms some dihedral angle with the plane CSD. Proceed with such consecutive rotations about each common side. If in the end the first side SA turns out to coincide with the last side SF, then the geometric figure thus formed (Figure 33) is called a **polyhedral angle**. The angles ASB, BSC, ..., ESA are called **plane angles**, or **faces**; their sides SA, SB, ..., SE **edges**; and their common vertex S the **vertex** of the polyhedral angle. Every edge of a polyhedral angle is at the same time the edge of some dihedral angle formed by two adjacent faces. Thus a polyhedral angle has as many edges, or dihedral angles, as it has plane angles. The smallest number of faces a polyhedral angle can have is equal to three, and such angles are called **trihedral**. There exist **tetrahedral, pentahedral**, etc. angles.

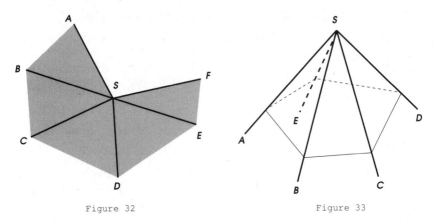

Figure 32   Figure 33

We will denote a polyhedral angle either by a single letter (S) marking its vertex, or by a string of letters ($SABCDE$) of which the first one denotes the vertex and the others label the edges in their consecutive order.

A polyhedral angle is called **convex**, if it lies entirely on one side of the planes of each of its faces. Thus, the polyhedral angle shown in Figure 33 is convex. On the contrary, the angle shown in Figure 34 is not convex, since it is situated on both sides of the plane ASB or of the plane BSC.

If we intersect all faces of a polyhedral angle by a plane, then in this plane a polygon is formed. In a convex polyhedral angle, such a polygon is also convex. *In the sequel, unless the opposite is specified, all polyhedral angles we consider will be assumed convex.*

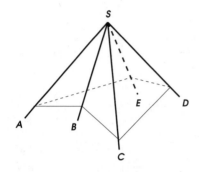

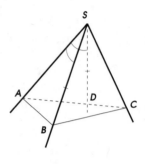

Figure 34   Figure 35

47. Theorem. *In a trihedral angle, each plane angle is smaller than the sum of the other two plane angles.*

In a trihedral angle $SABC$ (Figure 35), let the greatest of the plane angles be the angle ASC. In the interior of this angle, mark the angle ASD congruent to $\angle ASB$, and draw any line AC intersecting SD at some point D. Mark $SB = SD$ and connect B with A and C.

In $\triangle ABC$, we have:

$$AD + DC < AB + BC.$$

The triangles ASD and ASB are congruent since their angles at the vertex S are congruent and enclosed between respectively congruent sides, and hence $AD = AB$. Discarding the congruent summands AD and AB on each side of the above inequality we conclude that $DC < BC$. We note now that in the triangles BSC and DSC, two sides of one of them are respectively congruent to two sides of the other, while the third respective sides are not congruent. In this case, the angle opposite to the smaller of these sides is smaller, i.e.

$$\angle CSD < \angle CSB.$$

Adding to the left side of this inequality the angle ASD, and to the right side the angle ASB congruent to $\angle ASD$, we obtain the required

inequality:
$$\angle ASC < \angle ASB + \angle CSB.$$

Corollary. Subtracting from both sides of the latter inequality the angle ASB or the angle CSB, we obtain:

$$\angle ASC - \angle ASB < \angle CSB$$
$$\angle ASC - \angle CSB < \angle ASB.$$

Reading these inequalities from right to left, and also taking into account that the angle ASC, being the greatest of the three plane angles, is also greater than the difference of the other two, we conclude that *in a trihedral angle, each plane angle is greater than the difference of the other two plane angles.*

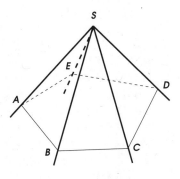

Figure 36

48. Theorem. *In a convex polyhedral angle, the sum of all the plane angles is smaller than*[3] $4d$.

Intersect all the faces of a convex polyhedral angle $SABCDE$ (Figure 36) by any plane. Then a convex n-gon $ABCDE$ will be formed in the plane of the cross-section. Applying the previous theorem to each of the trihedral angles whose vertices are A, B, C, D, and E, we find:

$$\angle ABC < \angle ABS + \angle CBS;$$
$$\angle BCD < \angle BCS + \angle DCS \text{ and so on.}$$

Add all these inequalities term-wise. On the left hand side, we obtain the sum of all angles of the polygon $ABCDE$, which is congruent to $2dn - 4d$, and on the right the sum of angles of the triangles

---

[3]Recall from Book I, that the measure of a right angle is denoted by d.

ABS, BCS, and so on, except those angles, which have the vertex S. Denoting the sum of the latter angles by the letter x, we find after the summation:

$$2dn - 4d < 2dn - x.$$

In the differences $2dn - 4d$ and $2dn - x$, the minuends are the same. Thus, in order for the first difference to be smaller than the second one, it is necessary that the first subtrahend $4d$ be greater than the second subtrahend x, i.e. $4d > x$.

49. Symmetric polyhedral angles. As we already know, vertical angles are congruent, as long as they are angles formed by lines or by planes. Let us find out if this statement still holds true for polyhedral angles.

Extend all edges of a polyhedral angle $SABCDE$ (Figure 37) past the vertex S, so that a new polyhedral angle $SA'B'C'D'E'$ is formed, which can be called **vertical** to the original one. It is not hard to see that in these polyhedral angles, all plane angles of as well as dihedral ones are respectively congruent, but the angles of either kind are positioned in the opposite order. Indeed, if we imagine an observer who is looking from the exterior of the first polyhedral angle at its vertex, we find that the edges SA, SB, SC, SD, SE of the first angle will appear to him ordered counter-clockwise. However if he is looking at the angle $SA'B'C'D'E'$ from its exterior, then the edges SA', SB', SC', SD', SE' will appear ordered clockwise.

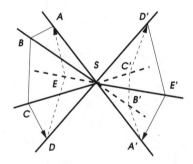

Figure 37

Polyhedral angles whose plane and dihedral angles are respectively congruent but are positioned in the opposite order cannot, generally speaking, be superimposed onto each other, and are therefore not congruent. Such polyhedral angles are often called **symmetric**. Symmetry of figures in space will be discussed in more detail in Section 4 of Chapter 2.

50. Theorem (tests for congruence of trihedral angles).

Two trihedral angles are congruent if they have:

(1) *a pair of congruent dihedral angles enclosed between two respectively congruent and similarly positioned plane angles,* or

(2) *a pair of congruent plane angles enclosed between two respectively congruent and similarly positioned dihedral angles.*

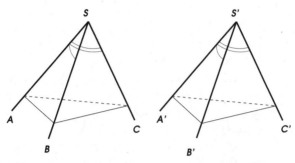

Figure 38

(1) Let S and S' be two trihedral angles (Figure 38) such that $\angle ASB = \angle A'S'B'$, $\angle ASC = \angle A'S'C'$ (and these respectively congruent angles are also positioned similarly), and the dihedral angle AS is congruent to the dihedral angle $A'S'$. Insert the angle S' into the angle S so that the vertices S' and S, edges $S'A'$ and SA, and planes $A'S'B'$ and ASB coincide. Then the edge $S'B'$ will merge with SB (since $\angle A'S'B' = \angle ASB$), the plane $A'S'C'$ will merge with ASC (since the dihedral angles are congruent), and the edge $S'C'$ will merge with the edge SC (since $\angle A'S'C' = \angle ASC$). Thus all respective edges of the trihedral angles become superimposed onto each other, and therefore the angles are congruent.

(2) The second test is proved similarly by superimposing.

EXERCISES

46. Show that every trihedral angle is convex.

47. Can a non-convex polyhedral angle have the sum of plane angles smaller than $2d$?

48. Give an example of a non-convex tetrahedral angle whose sum of plane angles is: (a) greater than $4d$; (b) smaller than $4d$; (c) $4d$.

49. How many of the planes angles of a convex tetrahedral angle can be obtuse?

50. Prove that: if a trihedral angle has two right plane angles then two of its dihedral angles are right. Conversely, if a trihedral angle has two right dihedral angles then two of its plane angles are right.

51. Prove that every plane angle of a tetrahedral angle is smaller than the sum of the other three.

52. Can symmetric polyhedral angles be congruent?

53. Prove that two trihedral angles are congruent if: (a) all their plane angles are right, or (b) all their dihedral angles are right.

54.⋆ Prove that a tetrahedral angle can be intersected by a plane in such a way that the cross section is a parallelogram.

55. In the interior of a trihedral angle, find the geometric locus of points equidistant from the faces.

56. Suppose that two dihedral angles with parallel edges have respectively perpendicular faces. Prove that either these dihedral angles are congruent, or their sum is congruent to $2d$ (i.e. to the sum of two right dihedral angles).

57. Suppose that from a point in the interior of a dihedral angle, perpendiculars are dropped to its faces. Prove that the angle between the perpendiculars is congruent to the angle supplementary to the linear angle.

58. Suppose that edges of one trihedral angle are perpendicular to the faces of another trihedral angle. Prove that faces of the first angle are perpendicular to the edges of the second.

59.⋆ Prove that in a trihedral angle, the sum of all dihedral angles is greater than $2d$, and the sum of each pair of dihedral angles is smaller than the sum of the third dihedral angle and $2d$.

60.⋆ Prove that in a (convex) polyhedral angle with n faces the sum of all dihedral angles is greater than $2dn - 4d$ (i.e. than the angle sum of a convex n-gon).

61.⋆ One of two polyhedral angles with the same vertex lies inside the other. Prove that the sum of plane angles of the latter one is greater than the sum of plane angles of the former. Does this remain true if one of the polyhedral angles is not required to be convex? Which one?

Chapter 2

POLYHEDRA

1 Parallelepipeds and pyramids

51. Polyhedra.[1] A **polyhedron** is a geometric solid bounded by polygons. The boundary polygons of a polyhedron are called its **faces**. A common side of two adjacent faces is called an **edge** of the polyhedron. When several faces meet at their common vertex, they form a polyhedral angle, and the vertex of the angle is called a **vertex** of the polyhedron. A straight segment connecting any two vertices, which do not lie in the same face, is called a **diagonal** of the polyhedron.

The smallest number of faces a polyhedron can have is four. Such a polyhedron can be cut out of a trihedral angle by a plane.

We will consider only those polyhedra which are **convex**, i.e. lie on one side of the plane of each of its faces.

52. Prisms. Take any polygon $ABCDE$ (Figure 39), and through its vertices, draw parallel lines not lying in its plane. Then on one of the lines, take any point (A') and draw through it the plane parallel to the plane $ABCDE$, and also draw a plane through each pair of adjacent parallel lines. All these planes will cut out a polyhedron $ABCDEA'B'C'D'E'$ called a **prism**.

The parallel planes $ABCDE$ and $A'B'C'D'E'$ are intersected by the lateral planes along parallel lines (§13), and therefore the quadrilaterals $AA'B'B$, $BB'C'C$, etc. are parallelograms. On the other hand, in the polygons $ABCDE$ and $A'B'C'D'E'$, corresponding sides are congruent (as opposite sides of parallelograms), and correspond-

---

[1] *Polyhedra* (or *polyhedrons*) is the plural of *polyhedron*.

29

ing angles are congruent (as angles with respectively parallel and similarly directed sides). Therefore these polygons are congruent.

Thus, a **prism** can be defined as a polyhedron two of whose faces are congruent polygons with respectively parallel sides, and all other faces are parallelograms connecting the parallel sides.

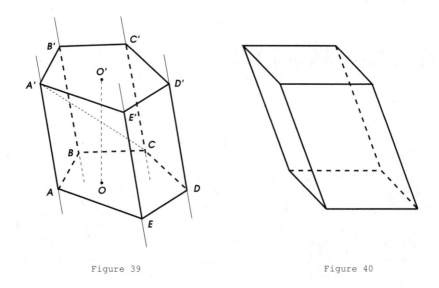

Figure 39   Figure 40

The faces ($ABCDE$ and $A'B'C'D'E'$) lying in parallel planes are called **bases** of the prism. The perpendicular OO' dropped from any point of one base to the plane of the other is called an **altitude** of the prism. The parallelograms $AA'B'C$, $BB'C'C$, etc. are called **lateral faces**, and their sides AA', BB', etc., connecting corresponding vertices of the bases, are called **lateral edges** of the prism. The segment $A'C$ shown in Figure 39 is one of the diagonals of the prism.

A prism is called **right** if its lateral edges are perpendicular to the bases (and **oblique** if they are not). Lateral faces of a right prism are rectangles, and a lateral edge can be considered as the altitude.

A right prism is called **regular** if its bases are regular polygons. Lateral faces of a regular prism are congruent rectangles.

Prisms can be **triangular**, **quadrangular**, etc. depending on what the bases are: triangles, quadrilaterals, etc.

53. Parallelepipeds are prisms whose bases are parallelograms (Figure 40). Just like general prisms, parallelepipeds can be right or oblique. A right parallelepiped is called **rectangular**[2] if its base is a rectangle (Figure 41). It follows from the definitions that:

(1) All six faces of a parallelepiped are parallelograms;

(2) The four lateral sides of a right parallelepiped are rectangles, while its bases are parallelograms;

(3) All six faces of a rectangular parallelepiped are rectangles.

The three edges of a rectangular parallelepiped meeting at a vertex are called its **dimensions**; one of them can be considered its length, another width, and the third height.

A rectangular parallelepiped whose three dimensions are all congruent to each other is called a **cube**. All faces of a cube are squares.

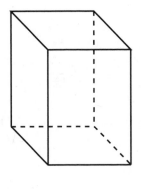

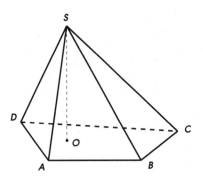

Figure 41   Figure 42

54. Pyramids. A **pyramid** is a polyhedron, of which one face (called its **base**) can be any polygon, and all other faces (called **lateral**) are triangles meeting at a common vertex.

In order to construct a pyramid, it suffices to take any polyhedral angle S (Figure 42), cut it by a plane $ABCD$ intersecting all the edges, and take the finite part $SABCD$.

The common vertex of the lateral faces is called the **vertex**, the edges adjacent to it **lateral edges** of the pyramid, and the perpendicular SO, dropped from the vertex to the base, its **altitude**.

A plane drawn through the vertex and any diagonal of the base (e.g. the diagonal BD, Figure 44) is called a **diagonal plane** of the

---

[2]Rectangular parallelepipeds are also known as **cuboids** or **boxes**.

pyramid. Identifying a pyramid by names of its vertices, one usually begins with the vertex, e.g. $SABCD$ (Figure 42).

Pyramids can be triangular, quadrangular, etc., depending on what the base is: a triangle, quadrilateral, etc. A triangular pyramid is also called a **tetrahedron** (Figure 43). All four faces of a tetrahedron are triangles.

A pyramid is called **regular** (Figure 44) if, firstly, its base is a regular polygon, and secondly, the altitude passes through the center of this polygon. In a regular pyramid, all lateral edges are congruent to each other (as slants with congruent projections). Therefore all lateral faces of a regular pyramid are congruent isosceles triangles. The altitude SM (Figure 44) of each of these triangles is called an **apothem**. All apothems of a regular pyramid are congruent.

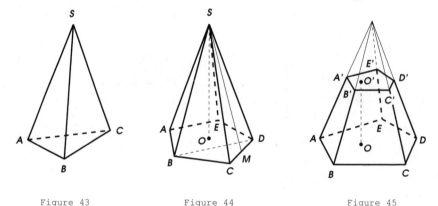

Figure 43   Figure 44   Figure 45

55. Frustum of a pyramid.   The part of a pyramid (Figure 45) contained between its base ($ABCDE$) and a section plane ($A'B'C'D'E'$) parallel to the base is called a **pyramidal frustum**. The parallel faces are called **bases**, and the segment OO' of the perpendicular dropped from any point of one base to the other, an **altitude** of the pyramidal frustum. A frustum of a regular pyramid is called a **regular pyramidal frustum**.

56. Theorem. *In a parallelepiped:*

(1) *opposite faces are congruent and parallel;*

(2) *all four diagonals intersect at their midpoints.*

(1) The bases $ABCD$ and $A'B'C'D'$ (Figure 46) are parallel and congruent by the very definition of parallelepipeds as a kind of prisms. The lateral faces $BB'C'C$ and $AA'D'D$ are parallel because two intersecting lines BB' and $B'C'$ in one of them are respectively

parallel to two lines AA' and $A'D'$ in the other (§12). These faces, being parallelograms, are congruent since $B'C' = A'D'$, $BB' = AA'$ (as opposite sides of parallelograms) and $\angle BB'C' = \angle AA'D'$ (as angles with respectively parallel and similarly directed sides).

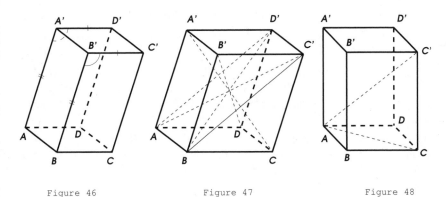

Figure 46   Figure 47   Figure 48

(2) Pick any two diagonals (e.g. AC' and BD', Figure 47), and draw the auxiliary lines AD' and BC'. Since the edges AB and $D'C'$ are parallel and congruent to the edge DC, they are parallel and congruent to each other. Therefore the figure $ABC'D'$ is a parallelogram in which the lines AC' and BD' are diagonals, and diagonals in any parallelogram bisect each other. Thus the diagonals BD' and AC' intersect at their midpoints. But the same applies to any pair of diagonals, e.g. to AC' and any of the remaining diagonals $B'D$ or $A'C$. Therefore each of these diagonals also intersects AC' at the midpoint and is itself bisected by the point of intersection. Thus all the diagonals pass through the same point — the midpoint of AC', and are bisected by it.

57. Theorem. *In a rectangular parallelepiped, the square of any diagonal* ($C'A$, Figure 48) *is equal to the sum of the squares of the dimensions.*

Drawing the diagonal AC of the base we obtain the triangles ACC' and ABC. They are both right triangles, the first one because the parallelepiped is right, and therefore the edge $C'C$ is perpendicular to the base, and the second one because the parallelepiped is rectangular, and hence its base is a rectangle. From these triangles, we find:

$$C'A^2 = AC^2 + C'C^2 \text{ and } AC^2 = AB^2 + BC^2.$$

Therefore
$$C'A^2 = AB^2 + BC^2 + C'C^2.$$

Corollary. *In a rectangular parallelepiped, all diagonals are congruent.*

58. Parallel cross sections of pyramids.

Theorem. *If a pyramid* (Figure 49) *is intersected by a plane parallel to the base, then:*

(1) *lateral edges and the altitude* (SM) *are divided by this plane into proportional parts;*

(2) *the cross section itself is a polygon* $(A'B'C'D'E')$ *similar to the base;*

(3) *the areas of the cross section and the base are proportional to the squares of the distances from them to the vertex.*

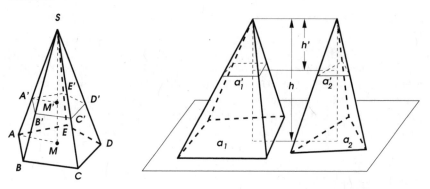

Figure 49   Figure 50

(1) The lines $A'B'$ and AB can be considered as intersection lines of two parallel planes (the base and the cross section) by a third plane ASB. Therefore $A'B' \| AB$ (§13). For the same reason, we have: $B'C' \| BC$, $C'D' \| CD$, etc., and $A'M' \| AM$. It follows from Thales' theorem that

$$\frac{SA'}{A'A} = \frac{SB'}{B'B} = \frac{SC'}{C'C} = \cdots = \frac{SM'}{M'M}.$$

(2) From similarity of the triangles ASB and $A'SB'$, and then BSC and $B'SC'$, we derive:

$$\frac{AB}{A'B'} = \frac{BS}{B'S}, \quad \frac{BS}{B'S} = \frac{BC}{B'C'}, \quad \text{and hence} \quad \frac{AB}{A'B'} = \frac{BC}{B'C'}.$$

Similarly, we obtain: $BC : B'C' = CD : C'D'$, as well as the proportionality of all other sides of the polygons $ABCDE$ and $A'B'C'D'E'$. These polygons also have congruent corresponding angles (as angles with parallel and similarly directed sides), and are therefore similar.

(3) Areas of similar polygons are proportional to the squares of corresponding sides (see Book I, §251). Since

$$\frac{AB}{A'B'} = \frac{AS}{A'S} = \frac{MS}{M'S}$$

(due to similarity of $\triangle ASM$ and $\triangle A'SM'$), we conclude that

$$\frac{\text{Area of } ABCDE}{\text{Area of } A'B'C'D'E'} = \frac{AB^2}{(A'B')^2} = \frac{MS^2}{M'S^2}.$$

Corollary 1. *If two pyramids with congruent altitudes are intersected by planes at the same distance from the vertices, the areas of the cross sections are proportional to the areas of the bases.*

Let a_1 and a_2 (Figure 50) be the areas of the bases of two pyramids, h the altitude of each of them, and a'_1 and a'_2 the areas of the cross sections parallel to the bases and drawn at the same distance h' from the vertices. According to the theorem, we have:

$$\frac{a'_1}{a_1} = \frac{(h')^2}{h^2} = \frac{a'_2}{a_2}, \quad \text{and hence} \quad \frac{a'_1}{a'_2} = \frac{a_1}{a_2}.$$

Corollary 2. If $a_1 = a_2$ then $a'_1 = a'_2$, i.e. *if bases of two pyramids with congruent altitudes are equivalent [3], then cross sections equidistant from the vertices are also equivalent.*

59. Lateral surface area of prisms.

Theorem. *The lateral surface area of a prism is equal to the product of a lateral edge and the perimeter of a perpendicular cross section.*

By a **perpendicular cross section** (Figure 51) of a prism, we mean the polygon $abcde$ obtained by intersecting all lateral faces of the prism by a plane perpendicular to the lateral edges. Sides of this polygon are perpendicular to the lateral edges (§§31, 20).

The lateral surface area of the prism is equal to the sum of areas of parallelograms. In each of them, a lateral edge can be considered as the base, and one of the sides of the perpendicular cross section as the altitude. Therefore the lateral surface area is equal to $AA' \cdot ab + BB' \cdot bc + CC' \cdot cd + DD' \cdot de + EE' \cdot ea = AA' \cdot (ab + bc + cd + de + ea)$.

---

[3]Recall that plane figures are called **equivalent** when they have equal areas.

Corollary. *The lateral surface area of a right prism is equal to the product of the perimeter of the base and the altitude,* because lateral edges of such a prism are congruent to the altitude, and its base can be considered as the perpendicular cross section.

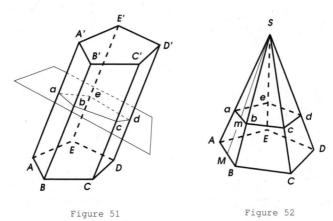

Figure 51   Figure 52

60. Lateral surface area of regular pyramids.

Theorem. *The lateral surface area of a regular pyramid is equal to the product of an apothem and the semiperimeter of the base.*

Let $SABCDE$ (Figure 52) be a regular pyramid, and SM its apothem. The lateral surface area of the pyramid is the sum of areas of congruent isosceles triangles. The area of one of them, e.g. ASB, is equal to $\frac{1}{2}AB \cdot SM$. If n is the number of triangles, then the lateral surface is equal to $\frac{1}{2}AB \cdot n \cdot SM$, where $\frac{1}{2}AB \cdot n$ is the semiperimeter of the base, and SM is the apothem.

Theorem. *The lateral surface area of a regular pyramidal frustum is equal to the product of an apothem and half the sum of the perimeters of the bases.*

The lateral surface area (Figure 52) of a regular pyramidal frustum $abcdeABCDE$ is the sum of areas of congruent isosceles trapezoids. The area of one of the trapezoids, e.g. $AabB$, is equal to $\frac{1}{2} \cdot (AB + ab) \cdot Mm$. If n is the number of trapezoids, then the lateral surface area is equal to

$$\frac{AB + ab}{2} \cdot Mm \cdot n = Mm \cdot \frac{AB \cdot n + ab \cdot n}{2},$$

where $AB \cdot n$ and $ab \cdot n$ are perimeters of the bases.

EXERCISES

62. Show that in a tetrahedron, or a parallelepiped, each face can be chosen for its base.

63. Compute the angle between diagonals of two adjacent faces of a cube. (Consider first the diagonals that meet, then skew ones.)

64. Prove that if every face of a polyhedron has an odd number of sides then the number of the faces is even.

65.* Prove that in every polyhedron all of whose faces are triangles there is an edge such that all plane angles adjacent to it are acute.

66.* Prove that in every tetrahedron, there is a vertex all of whose plane angles are acute.

67. Prove that in a tetrahedron, all faces are congruent if and only if all pairs of opposite edges are congruent.

68. Find a point equidistant from all faces of a given tetrahedron.

69.* Prove that a polyhedron is convex if and only if every segment with the endpoints in the interior of the polyhedron lies entirely in the interior.

70. Prove that faces, cross sections, and projections of convex polyhedra are convex polygons.

71. Compute the diagonal of the cube with the edge 1 *cm*.

72. In a cube, which of the two angles is greater: between two diagonals, or between a diagonal and an edge?

73. Prove that if two diagonals of a rectangular parallelepiped are perpendicular, then its dimensions are congruent to the sides of a right triangle, and *vice versa*.

74. Compute the length of a segment if its orthogonal projections to three pairwise perpendicular planes have lengths a, b, and c.

75.* Is a polyhedron necessarily a prism, if two of its faces are congruent polygons with respectively parallel sides, and all other faces are parallelograms? (First allow non-convex polyhedra.)

76.* Prove that if all diagonals in a prism are **concurrent** (i.e. pass through the same point), then this prism is a parallelepiped.

77. Prove that in a pyramidal frustum with quadrilateral bases, all diagonals are concurrent, and *vice versa*, if in a pyramidal frustum, all diagonals are concurrent, then its bases are quadrilateral.

78.* Find a parallelepiped three of whose edges lie on three given lines, of which no two lie in the same plane.

79. Compute the total surface area of a right prism whose altitude equals 1 *cm*, and the base is a right triangle with legs 3 *cm* and 4 *cm*.

80. The total surface area of a rectangular parallelepiped is equal to 1714 m^2, and the dimensions of the base are 25 m and 14 m. Compute the lateral surface area and the lateral edge.

81. In a rectangular parallelepiped with a square base and the altitude h, a cross section through two opposite lateral edges is drawn. Compute the total surface area of the parallelepiped, if the area of the cross section equals S.

82. A regular hexagonal pyramid has the altitude h and the side of the base a. Compute the lateral edge, apothem, lateral surface area, and total surface area.

83. Compute the total surface area of the tetrahedron all of whose edges have the same length a.

84. Compute the angle between lateral faces and the base of a regular pyramid whose lateral surface area is twice the area of the base.

85. Prove that if all lateral edges of a pyramid form congruent angles with the base, then the base can be inscribed into a circle.

86. Prove that if all lateral faces of a pyramid form congruent angles with the base, then the base can be circumscribed about a circle.

87. A regular hexagonal pyramid, which has the altitude 15 cm and the side of the base 5 cm, is intersected by a plane parallel to the base. Compute the distance from this plane to the vertex, if the area of the cross section is equal to $\frac{2}{3}\sqrt{3}$ cm^2.

88. The altitude of a regular pyramidal frustum with a square base is h, and the areas of the bases are a and b. Find the total surface area of the frustum.

89. The bases of a pyramidal frustum have areas 36 and 16. The frustum is intersected by a plane parallel to the bases and bisecting the altitude. Compute the area of the cross section.

90.* Through each edge of a cube, draw outside the cube the plane making 45° angles with the adjacent faces. Compute the surface area of the polyhedron bounded by these planes, assuming that the edges of the cube have length a. Is this polyhedron a prism?

91. Prove that if all altitudes of a tetrahedron are concurrent, then each pair of opposite edges are perpendicular, and *vice versa*.

92.* Prove that if one of the altitudes of a tetrahedron passes through the orthocenter of the opposite face, then the same property holds true for the other three altitudes.

93.* From a point in the interior of a polyhedron, perpendiculars to the planes of the faces are dropped. Prove that the foot of at least one of the perpendiculars lies in the interior of the face.

2   Volumes of prisms and pyramids

61. Main assumptions about volumes. A vessel of a certain shape can hold a certain amount of water. The amount can be measured and expressed quantitatively in "cubic" units, such as cm^3, m^3, ft^3, etc. Such measuring of solid shapes leads us to the geometric theory of volumes. Our assumptions about volumes express therefore, in an idealized form, properties of the water-holding capacity of vessels. Namely we will assume that volumes of geometric solids are expressed by *positive* numbers, and are defined for all polyhedra and, more generally, for all solids that can be partitioned into several polyhedra. Furthermore, we assume that the following properties hold true.

(1) *Congruent solids have equal volumes.*

(2) *The volume of a solid subdivided into several parts is equal to the sum of the volumes of these parts.*

(3) *The volume of the unit cube* (i.e. the cube whose edge is a unit of length) *is equal to 1* (in the corresponding cubic units).

Two solids that have equal volumes are called **equivalent**.

62. Theorem. *The volume of a rectangular parallelepiped is equal to the product of its dimensions.*

Let a, b, c be three numbers expressing the three dimensions of a rectangular parallelepiped in a certain unit of length. Let V be the number expressing the volume of the parallelepiped in the corresponding cubic unit. The theorem says that $V = abc$. In the proof, we consider the following three cases.

(i) The dimensions are expressed by *whole* numbers.

Let for example the dimensions be (Figure 53) $AB = a$, $BC = b$, and $BD = c$, where a, b, c are whole numbers (in Figure 53, $a = 4$, $b = 2$, and $c = 5$). Then the base of the parallelepiped contains ab unit squares. On each of them, a unit cube can be placed. Thus a layer of such cubes is obtained (as shown in Figure 53) containing ab unit cubes. Since the altitude of this layer is congruent to one unit of length, and the altitude of the parallelepiped contains c such units, the whole parallelepiped can be filled with c such layers. Therefore the volume of the parallelepiped is equal to abc cubic units.

(ii) The dimensions are expressed by *fractions*.

Let the dimensions of the parallelepiped be

$$a = \frac{m}{n}, \quad b = \frac{p}{q}, \quad c = \frac{r}{s}.$$

Bringing the fractions to a common denominator, nqs, we have:

$$a = \frac{mqs}{nqs}, \quad b = \frac{nps}{nqs}, \quad c = \frac{nqr}{nqs}.$$

Pick a new (auxiliary) unit of length congruent to the $1/nqs$-th part of the original unit. Then the dimensions of the parallelepiped, expressed by means of this new unit, are given by whole numbers, and therefore by the result of case (i) the volume is equal to their product

$$(mns) \cdot (nps) \cdot (nqr),$$

if measured by the new cubic unit. The number of such new cubic units contained in the original unit cube is equal to $(nqs)^3$, i.e. the new cubic unit is equal to the $1/(nqs)^3$-th part of the original one. Therefore the volume of the parallelepiped expressed in the original cubic units is equal to

$$\frac{1}{(nqs)^3} \cdot (mns)(nps)(nqr) = \frac{mqs}{nqs} \cdot \frac{nps}{nqs} \cdot \frac{nqr}{nqs} = abc.$$

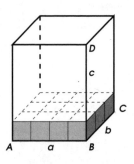

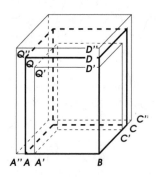

Figure 53   Figure 54

(iii) The dimensions are expressed by *arbitrary* real numbers.

Let the dimensions of the rectangular parallelepiped Q (Figure 54) be $AB = a$, $BC = b$ and $BD = c$, where a, b and c are positive real numbers, possibly irrational. Each of these numbers can be represented by an infinite decimal fraction. Take the finite decimal fractions: firstly α'_n, β'_n and γ'_n approximating a, b and c from below with the precision of $1/10^n$, and then α''_n, β''_n and γ''_n, approximating a, b and c from above with the same precision. On the lines AB,

BC and BD, mark the segments: firstly $BA' = \alpha'_n$, $BC' = \beta'_n$ and $BD' = \gamma'_n$, and then $BA'' = \alpha''_n$, $BC'' = \beta''_n$ and $BD'' = \gamma''_n$. We will have:

$$BA' \leq BA \leq BA'', \quad BC' \leq BC \leq BC'', \quad BD' \leq BD \leq BD''.$$

Next, build two auxiliary rectangular parallelepipeds: one (denoted Q') with the dimensions BA', BC' and BD', and the other (denoted Q'') with the dimensions BA'', BC'' and BD''. The parallelepiped Q' will lie in the interior of the parallelepiped Q, and the parallelepiped Q'' will contain the parallelepiped Q in its interior.

According to the result of case (ii), we will have:

$$\text{Volume of } Q' = \alpha'_n \beta'_n \gamma'_n, \quad \text{Volume of } Q'' = \alpha''_n \beta''_n \gamma''_n.$$

Now let us increase n. This means that we approximate a, b and c with greater and greater precision. As the number n increases indefinitely, the volume of Q' will obviously increase and (remaining bounded from above by the volume of Q) tend to a certain limit. This limit will be equal to the product of those limits to which the approximations α'_n, β'_n and γ'_n tend, i.e. to abc. On the other hand, as n increases indefinitely, the volume of Q'' will decrease and tend to the product of those limits to which α''_n, β''_n and γ''_n tend, i.e. to the same number abc. We conclude therefore that the volume of the parallelepiped Q is equal to the common limit abc, to which the volumes of the parallelepipeds Q' (contained in Q) and Q'' (containing Q) tend as n increases indefinitely.

Corollary. *The volume of a rectangular parallelepiped is equal to the product of the altitude and the area of the base.*

Indeed, if a and b denote dimensions of the base, then the third dimension c is the altitude, and its product with the area ab of the base is equal to the volume abc.

Remark. The ratio of two different cubic units is equal to the third power of the ratio of those units of length that serve as the edges of these unit cubes. For instance, the ratio of one cubic meter to one cubic centimeter is equal to 100^3, i.e. $1,000,000$. Similarly, one cubic yard contains $3^3 = 27$ cubic feet (Figure 55).

63. Lemma. *An oblique prism is equivalent to a right prism with base congruent to the perpendicular cross section of the oblique prism and with altitude congruent to its lateral edge.*

Suppose we are given an oblique prism $ABCDEA'B'C'D'E'$ (Figure 56). Extend all of its lateral edges and lateral faces in the same direction. On the extensions of any of the edges, e.g. AA', take a point a and draw through it the perpendicular cross section $abcde$. Then mark the segment $aa' = AA'$, and draw through the point a' another perpendicular cross section $a'b'c'd'e'$. Since the planes of the perpendicular cross sections are parallel, we have: $bb' = cc' = dd' = ee' = aa' = AA'$ (§14). Therefore the polyhedron ae' is the *right prism* (whose bases are the constructed perpendicular cross sections) described in the formulation of the lemma. Let us prove that it is equivalent to the given oblique prism.

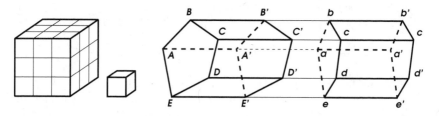

Figure 55   Figure 56

For this, we first notice that the polyhedra Ae and $A'e'$ are congruent. Indeed, the segments BB', CC', $\ldots$, ee' are congruent to AA' and have the same direction. Therefore, if we slide the second polyhedron along the lateral edges so that the vertex A' merges with the vertex A of the first polyhedron, then all the other corresponding vertices also merge: B' with B, C' with C, $\ldots$, e' with e. Thus the second polyhedron becomes superimposed onto the first one.

Now we notice that adding to the right prism ae' the polyhedron Ae, or adding to the oblique prism AE' the polyhedron $A'e'$, congruent to Ae, results in the same polyhedron Ae'. It follows that the two prisms ae' and AE' are equivalent.

64. Volumes of parallelepipeds.

Theorem. *The volume of a parallelepiped is equal to the product of the altitude and the area of the base.*

We have proved this theorem for *rectangular* parallelepipeds; we now prove it for *right* parallelepipeds, and then for oblique ones.

(i) Let (Figure 57) AC' be a right parallelepiped, i.e. its base $ABCD$ can be any parallelogram, and all lateral faces are rectangles. Take the lateral side $AA'B'B$ for a new base, so that the parallelepiped becomes oblique. Considering it as a special case of an oblique prism, we conclude from the lemma of §63 that this parallelepiped is equivalent to one with the altitude BC and the base a

perpendicular cross section $PQQ'P'$. The quadrilateral $PQQ'P'$ is a rectangle, because its angles are plane angles of right dihedral angles. Therefore the right parallelepiped, whose base is $PQQ'P$, must be rectangular, and hence its volume equal to the product of its three dimensions: QQ', PQ, and BC. But the product of PQ and BC expresses the area of the parallelogram $ABCD$. Thus

Volume of $AC' = $ (Area of $ABCD$) $\cdot QQ' = $ (Area of $ABCD$) $\cdot BB'$.

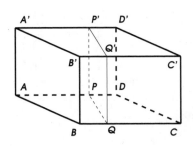

Figure 57   Figure 58

(ii) Let (Figure 58) AC' be an oblique parallelepiped. It is equivalent to such a right parallelepiped, whose altitude is the edge BC, and base a cross section $PQQ'P'$ perpendicular to the edges AD, BC, etc. But according to case (i), the volume of a right parallelepiped is equal to the product of the altitude and the area of the base, i.e.

Volume of $AC' = BC \cdot$ (Area of $PQQ'P'$).

If MM' is an altitude of the cross section $PQQ'P'$, then the area of $PQQ'P'$ is equal to $PQ \cdot MM'$, and therefore

Volume of $AC' = BC \cdot PQ \cdot MM'$.

But the product $BC \cdot PQ$ expresses the area of the parallelogram $ABCD$. It remains to show that the segment MM' is the altitude of the parallelepiped with respect to the base $ABCD$.

Indeed, the cross section $PQQ'P'$ is perpendicular to the line BC, which is therefore perpendicular to any line in the plane of the cross section, e.g. to MM'. On the other hand MM', being an altitude of the parallelogram $PQQ'P'$, is perpendicular to its base PQ. Thus

MM' is perpendicular to two intersecting lines (BC and PQ) in the plane $ABCD$, and therefore perpendicular to this plane.

Thus, the volume of the parallelepiped AC' is equal to the product of its altitude MM' and the area of the base $ABCD$.

65. Volumes of prisms.

Theorem. *The volume of a prism is equal to the product of the altitude and the area of the base.*

We will prove this for a *triangular* prism first, and then for an arbitrary one.

(i) Through a lateral edge AA' of a triangular prism $ABCA'B'C'$ (Figure 59), draw the plane parallel to the face $BB'C'C$, and through the edge CC' the plane parallel to the face $ABB'A'$, and then extend the planes of both bases up to their intersection with the drawn planes. We obtain the parallelepiped BD' divided by the diagonal plane $ACC'A'$ into two triangular prisms, of which the prism AC' is the given one. Let us prove that these prisms are equivalent. For

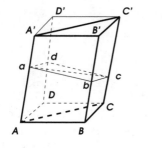   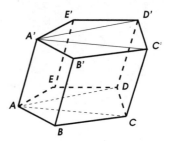

Figure 59   Figure 60

this, draw a perpendicular cross section $abcd$. It is a parallelogram which is divided by its diagonal ac into two congruent triangles. The given prism is equivalent to a right prism whose altitude is the edge AA' and base the triangle abc. The other triangular prism is equivalent to a right prism whose altitude is AA' and base the triangle adc. But two right prisms with congruent bases and altitudes can be superimposed onto each other, and are therefore congruent. Thus the prisms $ABCA'B'C'$ and $ADCA'D'C'$ are equivalent. It follows that the volume of the given prism is equal to *half* the volume of the parallelepiped BD'. If we denote by V the volume of the given prism, and by h its altitude, then we find:

$$V = \frac{(\text{Area of } ABCD) \cdot h}{2} = \frac{\text{Area of } ABCD}{2} \cdot h = (\text{Area of } ABC) \cdot h.$$

(ii) Through a lateral edge AA' (Figure 60) of an arbitrary given prism (Figure 60), draw all diagonal planes $AA'C'C$, $AA'D'D$. Then the given prism becomes divided into several triangular prisms. The sum of the volumes of these prisms is equal to the volume of the given one. If we denote by a_1, a_2, a_3 the areas of the bases of these triangular prisms, by h their common altitude, and by V the volume of the given prism, then we find:

$$V = a_1 \cdot h + a_2 \cdot h + a_3 \cdot h = (a_1 + a_2 + a_3) \cdot h = (\text{Area of } ABCDE) \cdot h.$$

Corollaries. (1) Comparing with the result of §63, we conclude that *the ratio of the area of the perpendicular cross section of an oblique prism to the area of the base is equal to the ratio of the altitude to the lateral edge.*

(2) *If a polygon (abcde in Figure 56) is the orthogonal projection of a given polygon (ABCDE), then the area of the projection is equal to the product of the area of the given polygon and the cosine of the angle between the planes of these polygons.*

Indeed, in the oblique prism shown in Figure 56, the ratio of the altitude to the lateral edge is the cosine of the angle between them. This angle, and the linear angle of the smaller of the dihedral angles, formed by the base and the perpendicular cross section, are congruent as angles with respectively perpendicular sides.

66. Cavalieri's principle. An Italian mathematician of the 17th century Bonaventura Cavalieri formulated the following proposition. *If two solids (bounded by — no matter — plane or curved surfaces) can be positioned in such a way that, for each plane parallel to a given plane, the cross sections of these solids by this plane are equivalent plane figures, then the volumes of these solids are equal.*

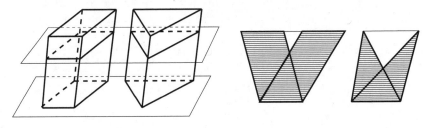

Figure 61   Figure 62

To justify Cavalieri's principle one needs methods that would go beyond elementary mathematics. We will merely verify the principle in several special cases.

For instance, the hypotheses of Cavalieri's principle are satisfied when two prisms (no matter — triangular or polygonal) have congruent altitudes and equivalent bases (Figure 61). As we already know, such prisms are equivalent. On the other hand, if such prisms are placed standing with their bases on the same plane, then every plane parallel to the bases and intersecting one of the prisms will intersect the other as well, and the cross sections will be equivalent (since they are congruent to the respective bases which are equivalent). Therefore Cavalieri's principle holds true in this special case.

Cavalieri's principle also applies to areas in plane geometry. Namely, *if two figures can be positioned so that for every line parallel to a given line, its intersections with the figures have equal lengths, then the figures are equivalent.* Two parallelograms or two triangles with congruent bases and congruent altitudes (Figure 62) are good illustrations of this principle.

The following lemma establishes Cavalieri's principle in the case of triangular pyramids.

67. Lemma. *Triangular pyramids with congruent altitudes and equivalent bases are equivalent.*

Placing the pyramids to stand on the same plane, divide their common altitude into an arbitrary number n congruent parts (see Figure 63 where $n = 4$) and draw through the division point planes parallel to the bases. Since the bases ABC and $A'B'C'$ are equivalent, the triangles formed as cross sections of one of the pyramids are respectively equivalent to the triangles formed as cross sections of the other pyramid (Corollary 2 in §58). In the interior of each pyramid, construct now a series of prisms such that: the triangular cross sections are their *upper* bases, the lateral edges are parallel to the edge SA in one of the pyramids and to the edge $S'A'$ in the other, and the altitude of each of the prisms is congruent to $1/n$-th of the altitude of the pyramids. There will be $n - 1$ such prisms in each pyramid. Denote the volumes of the prisms in the pyramid S by $p_1, p_2, \ldots, p_{n-1}$ in the order from the vertex to the base, and the volumes of the prisms in the pyramid S' by $p'_1, p'_2, \ldots, p'_n$ in the same order. Then we have:

$$p_1 = p'_1, \; p_2 = p'_2, \; \ldots, \; p_{n-1} = p'_{n-1},$$

because corresponding prisms of each pair have equivalent bases and congruent altitudes. Hence

$$p_1 + p_2 + \cdots + p_{n-1} = p'_1 + p'_2 + \cdots + p'_{n-1}.$$

Suppose now that n, i.e. the number of congruent parts into which we divided the altitude, increases indefinitely. Then both sides of the latter equality change, remaining equal to each other. Let us prove that each of the sides tends to a limit equal to the volume of the pyramid into which the prisms are inscribed, i.e. to the volume V of the pyramid S for the L.H.S., and to the volume V' of the pyramid S' for the R.H.S. Then the equality $V = V'$ of the limits will follow, since an infinite sequence can have at most one limit (Book I, §228).

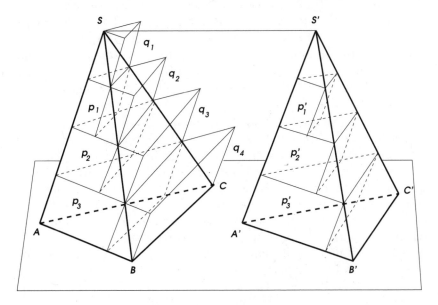

Figure 63

To prove that the L.H.S. tends to V as n increases indefinitely, construct in the pyramid S another series of prisms (situated partly outside the pyramid) such that: the triangular cross sections are their *lower* bases, while the lateral sides are parallel to SA and the altitudes are congruent to $1/n$-th of the altitude of the pyramid, as before. There will be n such prisms. Denote their volumes by $q_1, q_2, \ldots, q_n$ in the order from the vertex to the base. It is not hard to see that:

$$q_1 = p_1, \quad q_2 = p_2, \quad \ldots, \quad q_{n-1} = p_n.$$

Therefore:

$$(q_1 + q_2 + \cdots + q_{n-1} + q_n) - (p_1 + p_2 + \cdots + p_{n-1}) = q_n.$$

Since the pyramid S is covered by the n prisms entirely, we have:

$$p_1 + p_2 + \cdots + p_{n-1} < V < q_1 + q_2 + \cdots + q_n,$$

and hence

$$0 < V - (p_1 + p_2 + \cdots + p_{n-1}) < q_n.$$

As the number n increases indefinitely, the volume q_n of the bottom prism tends to 0 (because its altitude tends to 0 while the base ABC remains the same). Thus the difference $V - (p_1 + p_2 + \cdots + p_{n-1})$, remaining positive, tends to 0 as well. By the very definition of limit, this means that the sum $p_1 + p_2 + \cdots + p_{n-1}$ tends to V.

Obviously, the same argument applies to any triangular pyramid, e.g. to S', and we conclude that the sum $p_1' + p_2' + \cdots + p_{n-1}'$ tends to the volume V' of the pyramid S'. As we have noticed earlier, this means that $V = V'$, i.e. the two pyramids are equivalent.

Remark. The need for such an elaborate argument involving limits arises from the fact that two equivalent solids cannot be so easily transformed into one another by cutting one into pieces and reassembling them to form the other, as it can be done with equivalent polygons in plane geometry. Namely, it turns out there exist equivalent tetrahedra (in particular, those with equivalent bases and congruent altitudes) which are not **scissors-congruent**, i.e. cannot be cut into a *finite* number of respectively congruent polyhedral pieces. This impossibility result (which remains true even if adding the same auxiliary polyhedral pieces to both solids is allowed before cutting) was obtained in 1901 by a German mathematician **Max Dehn** as his solution to the so-called **Hilbert's 3rd Problem**. It was perhaps the most approachable of the 23 challenging mathematical problems (of which some still remain unsolved) presented by **David Hilbert** to the International Congress of Mathematicians in 1900.

68. Volumes of pyramids.

Theorem. *The volume of any pyramid is equal to the product of the area of the base and a third of the altitude.*

We first prove this theorem for *triangular* pyramids, and then for *polygonal.*

(i) On the base of a triangular pyramid $SABC$ (Figure 64), construct the prism $ABCSDE$ such that its altitude is congruent to the altitude of the pyramid, and one of the lateral edges coincides with the edge AS. Let us prove that the volume of the pyramid is equal to 1/3-rd of the volume of the prism. For this, remove the part of the prism occupied by the pyramid. The remaining part is the quadrangular pyramid $SBCED$ with the vertex S and the base

BCED. Divide this pyramid by the plane drawn through the vertex
S and the diagonal *DC* of the base into two triangular pyramids.
They have the same vertex *S* and congruent bases *BCD* and *CDE*
lying in the same plane, and are therefore equivalent according to the
lemma proved above. Compare one of them, *SBCD*, with the given
pyramid *SABC*. Taking the point *C* for the common vertex of these
pyramids, we see that they have bases *SAB* and *SDB*, which are
congruent and lie in the same plane. Therefore, by the same lemma,
these two pyramids are also equivalent. Thus the prism *ABCSDE*
is divided into 3 equivalent pyramids *SABC*, *SBCD*, and *SCDE*.
If we denote the volume of the given pyramid by *V*, the area of the
base *ABC* by *a*, and the altitude by *h*, we find:

$$V = \frac{\text{Volume of } ABCSDE}{3} = \frac{a \cdot h}{3} = a \cdot \frac{h}{3}.$$

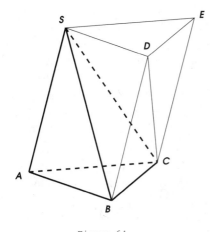
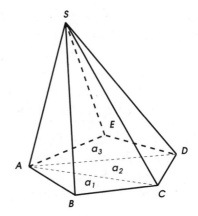

Figure 64   Figure 65

(ii) Through any vertex *A* (Figure 65) of the base of a polygonal
pyramid *SABCDE*, draw all diagonals *AC*, *AD*. Then draw section
planes through the edge *SA* and each of these diagonals. These
planes divide the polygonal pyramid into several triangular ones,
which have the same altitude as the given one. Denote this altitude
by *h*, and the areas of the bases of these triangular pyramids by
a_1, a_2, a_3. Then from part (i) we have:

$$\text{Volume of } SABCDE = a_1 \cdot \frac{h}{3} + a_2 \cdot \frac{h}{3} + a_3 \cdot \frac{h}{3} = (a_1 + a_2 + a_3) \cdot \frac{h}{3} = a \cdot \frac{h}{3},$$

where $a = a_1 + a_2 + a_3$ is the total area of the base of the given
pyramid.

EXERCISES

94. Compute the volume of a regular triangular prism whose lateral edge is l and the side of the base is a.

95. Express the volume of a rectangular parallelepiped in terms of the diagonals x, y, and z of the faces.

96. Compute the volume of a regular triangular pyramid whose lateral edge is l and the side of the base is a.

97.* Compute the volume of a parallelepiped all of whose faces are congruent rhombi with the side a and an angle $60°$.

98. Compute the volume of a pyramid, if lateral edges make the angle $60°$ with the plane of the base, which is a right triangle with the hypotenuse c and an angle $30°$.

99. In a pyramid with the altitude h, a plane parallel to the base is drawn that dissects the pyramid into two equivalent parts. Compute the distance of this plane from the vertex.

100. Compute the volume and lateral surface area of a regular hexagonal pyramid whose altitude has length h and makes the angle $30°$ with the apothem.

101. On the edges of a trihedral angle $SABC$, all three of whose plane angles are right, the segments $SA = a$, $SB = b$, and $SC = c$ are marked, and a plane is drawn through the points A, B, and C. Compute the volume of the pyramid $SABC$.

102. Compute the volume of a triangular pyramid all of whose lateral faces are perpendicular to each other and have areas a^2, b^2, and c^2.

103. Compute the volume of a triangular pyramid, if each lateral edge makes the angle $45°$ with the base, whose sides are a, b, and c.

104.* Compute the volume of a triangular prism (possibly oblique) if the area of one of its lateral faces is S, and the distance from the plane of this face to the opposite edge is d.

105.* Compute the volume of a right triangular prism whose base has the area $4\ cm^2$, and the lateral faces $9\ cm^2$, $10\ cm^2$, and $18\ cm^2$.

106.* Compute the volume of a regular quadrangular pyramid whose base has the edge a, and whose plane angles at the vertex have the same measure as the angles between lateral edges and the base.

107. A pyramidal frustum whose bases are regular hexagons with the sides $a = 23\ cm$ and $b = 17\ cm$ respectively, has the volume $V = 1465\ cm^3$. Compute the altitude of the frustum.

108. Prove that the volume of a pyramidal frustum is equal to the sum of the volumes of three pyramids which have the same altitude as the altitude of the frustum, and have areas of the bases equal respectively to: the area of the upper base, the area of the lower base, and their geometric mean.

109. Prove that the segments into which the plane, bisecting the dihedral angle AB of a tetrahedron $ABCD$, divides the opposite edge CD are proportional to the areas of the faces ABC and ABD.

110.* Does there exist a tetrahedron whose altitudes are 1, 2, 3, and 6 *cm* long?

Hint: Use Corollary 2 from §65.

3 Similarity of polyhedra

69. Definition. Two polyhedra are called **similar** if they have respectively congruent polyhedral angles and respectively similar and similarly positioned faces. For example, any two cubes are similar. Corresponding elements of similar polyhedra are called **homologous**.

It follows from the definition, that *in similar polyhedra:*

(1) *homologous dihedral angles are congruent and similarly positioned,* because the polyhedral angles are congruent;

(2) *homologous edges are proportional,* because in each of the two similar faces the ratios between homologous edges are the same, and in each polyhedron adjacent faces have an edge in common.

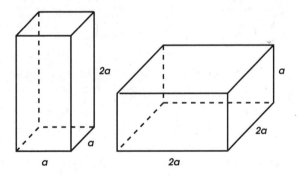

Figure 66

In the example in Figure 66, two rectangular parallelepipeds with square bases (and dimensions: one — $a, a, 2a$, the other — $2a, 2a, a$) have respectively congruent polyhedral angles, and respectively similar faces. These parallelepipeds are *not* similar, because lateral faces

are positioned differently (namely, their shorter edges are adjacent to
the bases in one parallelepiped, and their longer ones in the other). In
particular, there is no proportionality between corresponding edges
of these polyhedra.

To construct polyhedra similar to any given one, let us introduce
homothety in space.

70. Homothety. Given a geometric figure Φ (Figure 67), a
point S, and a positive number k, one defines another figure, Φ',
homothetic to Φ with respect to the **center of homothety** S with
the **homothety coefficient** k. Namely, pick a point A in the figure
Φ, and mark on the ray SA the point A' such that $SA' : SA = k$.
When this construction is applied to every point A of the figure Φ,
the geometric locus of the corresponding points A' is the figure Φ'
homothetic to Φ.

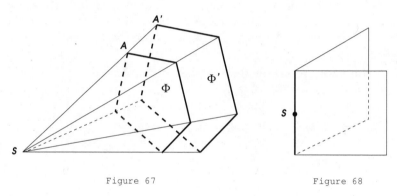

Figure 67   Figure 68

Clearly, the figure Φ is obtained from the figure Φ' by the homothety with the same center S and the homothety coefficient reciprocal
to k.

It is easy to see that the figure, homothetic to a given plane with
respect to any center not lying in it, is another plane parallel to the
given one.

Some figures can be homothetic to themselves even if the homothety coefficient $k \neq 1$. For example, the figure homothetic to a
dihedral angle (Figure 68) with respect to any center S lying on its
edge, is the dihedral angle itself. Likewise, any polyhedral angle is
obviously homothetic to itself with respect to the center of homothety
chosen at its vertex (Figure 67).

Remark. One can define homothety with a negative coefficient
k the way it was done in plane geometry, i.e. by requiring that the

point A' homothetic to A lies not on the ray SA, but on the extension of it beyond the center S. It is not hard to see that in the case of a negative homothety coefficient, the figure homothetic to a given polyhedral angle with respect to its vertex is the polyhedral angle *symmetric* to the given one in the sense of §49.

71. Lemma. **Two geometric figures homothetic to a given one with the same homothety coefficients but with respect to two different centers are congruent to each other.**

Indeed, let S and S' (Figure 69) be two centers of homothety, and let A be any point of the given figure. Denote by B and B' the points obtained from A by the homothety with the same coefficient k with respect to the centers S and S' respectively. We will assume that $k > 1$. The case where $k < 1$ (including the negative values) is very similar and will be left to the reader as an exercise. In the triangles SAS' and BAB', which lie in the same plane, the angles at the vertex A are congruent (as vertical), and the sides adjacent to the these angles are proportional. Indeed, since $BS : AS = k = B'S' : AS'$, we have: $BA : SA = k - 1 = B'A : S'A$. Therefore the triangles are similar, and in particular $\angle B'BS = \angle BSS'$, and $BB' : SS' = k - 1$. Thus the segment BB' is parallel to SS', the length of it is equal to $k - 1$ times the length of SS', and the direction of it is *opposite* to the direction of SS'. (In the case where $k < 1$, the direction will be the same.)

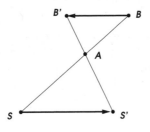

Figure 69

We conclude that by taking the point B homothetic to A with respect to the center S, then moving it in the direction parallel and opposite to the direction of the segment connecting S with S', and placing it at the distance $(k - 1) \cdot SS'$ from B, we obtain the point B' homothetic to A with respect to the center S'.

In this argument, A could be any point of the given figure. Thus, if Φ and Φ' are the figures homothetic to the given one with the same coefficient $k > 1$ but with respect to two different centers S and S', then the figure Φ can be superimposed onto the figure Φ' by moving Φ as a whole in the direction parallel and opposite to SS' through the distance $(k-1) \cdot SS'$. Thus Φ and Φ' are congruent.

72. Remark on translations. The operation of moving all points of a geometric figure by a given distance in the direction parallel to a given segment is a geometric transformation called **translation**. It generalizes to the case of space geometry the concept of translation on the plane described in Book I, §101.

For example, translating a given polygon $ABCDE$ (Figure 70) in a direction not parallel to its plane, we obtain another polygon $A'B'C'D'E'$, congruent and parallel to the given one. The segments AA', BB', etc. are parallel, congruent and similarly directed. Therefore the quadrilaterals $AA'B'B$, $BB'C'C$, etc. are parallelograms, and thus the given and translated polygons are two bases of the same prism AE'.

Using the concept of translation, our proof of the lemma can be summarized as the following statement about geometric transformations of figures: two homotheties with the same coefficient but different centers differ by an appropriate translation.

73. Corollaries. (1) *A polyhedral angle homothetic to a given one with a positive homothety coefficient is congruent to it.* Indeed, when the center of homothety is the vertex, the homothetic angle coincides with the given one; however, according to the lemma, the choice of another center gives rise to a congruent polyhedral angle.

(2) *A polygon homothetic to a given one is similar to it.* Indeed, this is true in plane geometry, i.e. when the center of homothety lies in the plane of the polygon. Therefore this remains true for any center due to the lemma (since polygons congruent to similar ones are similar).

(3) *A polyhedron obtained from a given one by a homothety with a positive coefficient is similar to it.* It is obvious that corresponding elements of homothetic polyhedra are positioned similarly with respect to each other, and it follows from the previous two corollaries that the polyhedral angles of such polyhedra are respectively congruent and corresponding faces similar.

74. Theorem. *If two polyhedra are similar, then each of them is congruent to a polyhedron homothetic to the other.*

Since polyhedral angles at homologous vertices of similar polyhedra are congruent, we can superimpose one of the polyhedral angles of the first polyhedron onto the homologous polyhedral angle of the second. Let $SABCDE$ (Figure 71) be the given polyhedron P, and let $SA'B'C'D'E'$ be the polyhedron P' similar to it and positioned in such a way that one pair of homologous polyhedral angles of both polyhedra coincide at the vertex S. Let k be the ratio $SA' : SA$ of homologous edges SA and SA'. We will prove that the polyhedron Q homothetic to P with respect to the center S with the homothety coefficient k coincides with P'. For this, note that respective edges of the polyhedra Q and P' are congruent, since they are proportional with the same coefficient k to the homologous edges of P. Therefore the endpoints A', B', C', and D' of the edges SA', SB', SC', and SD' of the polyhedron P' are vertices of the polyhedron Q as well. Consequently the polygons $SA'B', SB'C', SC'D'$, and $SD'A'$ are common faces of both polyhedra. Furthermore, since all homologous dihedral angles of Q and P' are congruent, the planes of the faces of Q adjacent to the edges $A'B'$ and $B'C'$ coincide with $A'B'E'$ and $B'C'E'$. Thus the polyhedral angles of Q and P' with the vertex B' coincide. Similarly to the way we compared edges and faces of the polyhedra Q and P' adjacent to their common polyhedral angle S, we can now proceed with their polyhedral angle B'. For example, the ray $B'E'$ is an edge of this polyhedral angle in both polyhedra, and since their respective edges are congruent, the endpoint E' of the edge $B'E'$ is their common vertex. So, we have found that the polyhedra Q and P' coincide since they have the same vertices. (Should Q and P' have more elements than those shown in Figure 71, we could consecutively compare their respective faces, edges, and vertices, and conclude that they all coincide.)

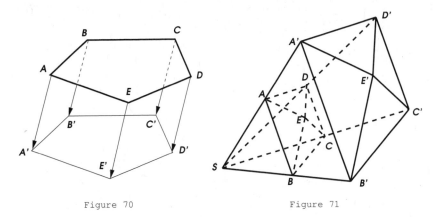

Figure 70   Figure 71

Thus the polyhedron similar to the given polyhedron P is congruent to the polyhedron Q homothetic to P.

75. Similarity of arbitrary geometric figures. One can give the following general definition of similarity: two geometric figures are **similar** if one of them is congruent to a figure homothetic to the other. The lemma of §72 shows that the position of the center of homothety in this definition is irrelevant: when a given figure becomes congruent to another after application of homothety with one center, it becomes congruent to it after homothety with any other center, provided that the coefficient of homothety remains the same. Thus, this definition fully expresses the idea of similarity as "being of the same shape but possibly different scale."

To maintain consistency with the definition of similar polyhedra given in §69, we need to assume that the homothety coefficients in the definition of arbitrary similar figures are positive. Then the previous theorem together with Corollary 3 of §73 show that two polyhedra are similar in this new sense whenever they are similar in the old sense, and *vice versa*.

76. Theorem. *In a pyramid* $(SABCDE$, *Figure 72), if a cross section parallel to the base is drawn, then it cuts off another pyramid* $(SA'B'C'D'E')$ *similar to the given one.*

According to part (1) of the theorem in §58, the lateral sides of the pyramids are proportional. Set $k = SA' : SA$, and apply to the given pyramid the homothety with the center S and coefficient k. Then the resulting figure will be a polyhedron with the vertices A', B', C', D', E', and S, i.e. it will be the pyramid $SA'B'C'D'E'$. Since homothetic polyhedra are similar, the theorem follows.

77. Theorem. *Surface areas of similar polyhedra have the same ratio as the squares of homologous edges.*

Let $A_1, A_2, \ldots, A_n$ denote the areas of faces of one of the similar polyhedra, and $a_1, a_2, \ldots, a_n$ the areas of the homologous faces of the other. Let L and l be the lengths of any two homologous edges. Then, due to similarity of homologous faces and proportionality of homologous edges, we have:

$$\frac{a_1}{A_1} = \frac{l^2}{L^2}, \; \frac{a_2}{A_2} = \frac{l^2}{L^2}, \; \ldots, \; \frac{a_n}{A_n} = \frac{l^2}{L^2}.$$

From properties of equal ratios, it follows:

$$\frac{a_1 + a_2 + \cdots + a_n}{A_1 + A_2 + \cdots + A_n} = \frac{l^2}{L^2}.$$

78. Theorem. *Volumes of similar polyhedra have the same ratio as the cubes of homologous edges.*

Consider first the case of pyramids. Let $SABCDE$ (Figure 72) be one of the given pyramids, L be the length of one of its edges, e.g. SA, and $l < L$ be the length of the homologous edge of the pyramid similar to it. On the altitude SO of the given pyramid, take the point O' such that $SO' : SO = l : L$, and draw through O' the cross section parallel to the base. Then the pyramid $SA'B'C'D'E'$, cut off by this plane, is homothetic to the first given pyramid with the homothety coefficient equal to $l : L$ and is therefore congruent to the second given pyramid. Let us denote by V and v the volumes of the pyramids $SABCDE$ and $SA'B'C'D'E'$ respectively, and prove that $v : V = l^3 : L^3$. For this we note that, according to the theorem of §58, the altitudes of these pyramids are proportional to their lateral edges, and the bases are similar polygons. Therefore, if a and a' denote the areas of the bases $ABCDE$ and $A'B'C'D'E'$, then

$$\frac{SO'}{SO} = \frac{l}{L}, \text{ and } \frac{a'}{a} = \frac{l^2}{L^2}.$$

Since $V = \frac{1}{3}a \cdot SO$ and $v = \frac{1}{3}a' \cdot SO'$, we find:

$$\frac{v}{V} = \frac{a'}{a} \cdot \frac{SO'}{SO} = \frac{l^2}{L^2} \cdot \frac{l}{L} = \frac{l^3}{L^3}.$$

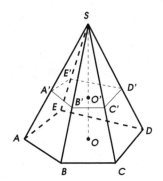

Figure 72

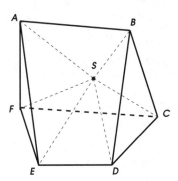

Figure 73

Suppose now that we are given two similar polyhedra with volumes V and v respectively, and with a pair of homologous edges of lengths L and l. In the interior of the first polyhedron, pick a point S (Figure 73), connect it with all vertices A, B, C, etc., and draw planes SAB, SBC, etc. through the point S and each edge of the polyhedron. Then the planes partition the polyhedron into pyramids

$SABCF$, $SBCD$, etc., which have the common vertex S, and whose bases are faces of the given polyhedron.[4] Let $V_1, V_2, \ldots, V_n$ be the volumes of the pyramids. If one applies the homothety with the center S and the coefficient equal to $l : L$, a polyhedron congruent to the second given one is obtained, partitioned into pyramids homothetic to $SABCF$, $SBCD$, etc. previously constructed. Let $v_1, v_2, \ldots, v_n$ be the respective volumes of these pyramids. Then

$$\frac{v_1}{V_1} = \frac{l^3}{L^3}, \; \frac{v_2}{V_2} = \frac{l^3}{L^3}, \; \ldots, \; \frac{v_n}{V_n} = \frac{l^3}{L^3},$$

and therefore,

$$\frac{v}{V} = \frac{v_1 + v_2 + \cdots + v_n}{V_1 + V_2 + \cdots + V_n} = \frac{l^3}{L^3}.$$

EXERCISES

111. Prove that two regular n-gonal pyramids are similar if and only if their plane angles at the vertex are congruent.

112. Find out which regular prisms are similar.

113. Prove that two pyramids are similar if the base and a lateral face of one of them and the base and a lateral face of the other are respectively similar, form respectively congruent dihedral angles, and are similarly positioned.

114. The same — about two prisms.

115. Show that a figure homothetic to a line (or a plane) with respect to a center of homothety not lying in it, is a line (respectively a plane) parallel to it.

116. Provide the proof of the lemma of §71 in the case of the homothety coefficient $k < 1$.

117. Prove that if one of two figures is congruent to a figure homothetic to the other, then *vice versa*, the other figure is congruent to a figure homothetic to the first one.

118. Prove that similar polyhedra of equal volume (or equal surface area) are congruent.

119. Given a cube with the edge a, find the edge x of another cube whose volume is twice the volume of the given one.

---

[4]Recall our convention to consider only *convex* polyhedra. In the case of nonconvex polyhedra, the theorem holds true, but the partitioning procedure should begin with dividing into convex polyhedra.

Remark. This problem of **doubling the cube**, known since antiquity, is easily solved by computation (namely, $x = \sqrt[3]{2a^3} = \sqrt[3]{2}a = a \times 1.259921\ldots$), but it cannot be solved by a straightedge and compass construction.

120. In what ratio should a plane parallel to the base of a pyramid divide its altitude so that the volumes of the parts into which the plane divides the pyramid have the ratio $m : n$?

121. A pyramid with the altitude h is divided by two planes parallel to the base into three parts whose volumes have the ratio $l : m : n$. Find the distances of these planes from the vertex.

122. Compute the volumes of two similar polyhedra, if their total volume is V, and their homologous edges have the ratio $m : n$.

4 Symmetries of space figures

79. Central symmetry. Two geometric figures are called **symmetric** about a point O if to every point A of one of the figures there corresponds a point A' of the other figure such that the midpoint of the segment AA' is the point O. The point O is called the **center of symmetry** of the figures.

Thus, in order to find the figure Φ' symmetric about the center O to a given figure Φ, one needs for every point A of the figure Φ, to extend the line AO past the center O and mark on the extension the segment OA' congruent to AO. Then the figure Φ' is the geometric locus of all points A' thus obtained.

We have encountered examples of centrally symmetric figures in §49, when we described the polyhedral angle symmetric to a given one about the vertex. Also, central symmetry is a special case of homothety with negative coefficients: the figure homothetic with the homothety coefficient $k = -1$ to a given figure is centrally symmetric to it about the center of homothety.

In centrally symmetric figures, certain homologous elements, such as segments, plane angles, or dihedral angles, are congruent. However the figures as wholes are not necessarily congruent, because generally speaking they cannot be superimposed onto each other. We have seen this phenomenon in the example of symmetric polyhedral angles.

Yet sometimes centrally symmetric figures are congruent, but the elements being superimposed are non-homologous. For instance, consider a trihedral angle with the vertex O and edges OX, OY and OZ (Figure 74) all of whose plane angles are right. Consider the angle

$OX'Y'Z'$ symmetric to *it*. Rotating the angle $OX'Y'Z'$ about the line XX' until the ray OZ' coincides with the ray OZ, and then rotating the resulting angle about the line OZ, we can superimpose the angle $OX'Y'Z'$ onto $OXYZ$. However the ray OX' then merges with the ray OY, and OY' with OX. However, if we rotate the angle $OX'Y'Z'$ about the line ZZ' until the rays OX' and OY' coincide with OX and OY respectively, then the rays OZ and OZ' turn out to have opposite directions.

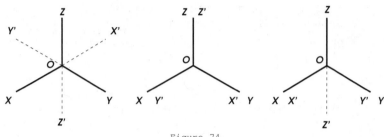

Figure 74

If the geometric figure symmetric to a given one about a certain center coincides with the given figure, one says that the given figure has a center of symmetry. For example, *any parallelepiped has a center of symmetry,* namely the intersection point of the diagonals (§56).

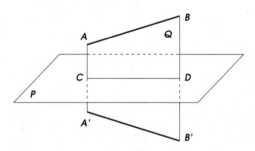

Figure 75

80. Bilateral symmetry. Two geometric figures are called **symmetric** about a given plane P, if to every point A of one of the figures there corresponds a point A' of the other, such that the segment AA' is perpendicular to the plane P and is bisected by the intersection point with it. The plane P is called the **plane of symmetry** of the figures.

In figures symmetric about a plane, corresponding segments, and plane or dihedral angles are congruent. For example, if A and B are any two points of a given figure, and A' and B' are the points symmetric to them about a plane P (Figure 75), then the segments AB and $A'B'$ are congruent. Indeed, since the lines AA' and BB' are perpendicular to the plane P, they are parallel to each other, and in particular lie in the same plane, Q, perpendicular to P. Inside this plane, the points A and B are symmetric, about the line of intersection of the planes P and Q, to the points A' and B' respectively (because AA' and BB' are perpendicular to this line and are bisected by it). Therefore $AB = A'B'$.

As in the case of central symmetry, figures symmetric about a plane are not necessarily congruent. Examples of symmetric figures are obtained by reflecting any object in a mirror: every figure is symmetric to its mirror reflection with respect to the plane of the mirror.

If a geometric figure coincides with the figure symmetric to it about a certain plane (or, in other words, can be divided into two parts symmetric about this plane), then the figure is said to have a plane of symmetry, or is symmetric **bilaterally**.

Bilaterally symmetric objects are frequently found in the household (e.g. chairs, beds, etc.) and in nature. For instance, the human body has a plane of bilateral symmetry dividing it into the left and right sides. By the way, this provides a convincing example of symmetric figures which are not congruent. Namely, the left and right hands are symmetric, but cannot be superimposed, as it is clear from the fact that the same glove does not fit both hands.

Symmetry about a line. Two figures are called symmetric about a line l if to every point A of one of the figures there corresponds a point A' of the other such that the segment AA' is perpendicular to the line l, intersects it, and is bisected by the point of intersection. The line l is called the **axis of symmetry** of the 2nd order.

It follows from the definition, that if two geometric figures symmetric about a line are intersected by any plane perpendicular to this line (at some point O) then the cross sections of the figures are plane figures symmetric about the point O.

Furthermore, it follows easily that two solids symmetric about a line can be superimposed by rotating one of them $180°$ about the line. Indeed, imagine all possible planes perpendicular to the axis of symmetry. Each of these planes contains two cross sections symmetric about the point of intersection of the plane with the axis. If one moves the plane along itself by rotating it in space 180° about the axis, then the first figure becomes superimposed onto the second. This holds true for every cross section perpendicular to the axis. Since simultaneous rotation of all cross sections through the angle of 180° is equivalent to rotating the whole figure 180° about the axis, our statement follows.

If a figure, obtained from a given one by rotating 180° about a certain line, coincides with the given figure, one says that it has an axis of symmetry of the 2nd order. The name reflects the fact that in the process of rotation by 360° about an "axis of symmetry of the 2nd order" the rotated figure will occupy its original position twice.

Here are some examples of solids possessing axes of symmetry of the 2nd order:

(1) A regular pyramid with an even number of lateral faces. The axis of symmetry is the altitude.

(2) A rectangular parallelepiped. It has three axes of symmetry of the 2nd order, namely the lines connecting the centers of opposite faces.

(3) A regular prism. If the number n of lateral faces is even, then the prism has $n + 1$ axes of symmetry of the 2nd order, namely $\frac{1}{2}n$ lines connecting the midpoints of opposite lateral edges, and $\frac{1}{2}n + 1$ lines connecting the centers of opposite faces, including the bases. If the number n of lateral faces is odd, then the prism has n axes of symmetry of the 2nd order, namely each line connecting the midpoint of a lateral edge and the center of the opposite lateral face.

81. Relations between central, bilateral and axial symmetries.

Theorem. *If two figures are symmetric to a given figure, one about a point* $(O$, Figure 76$)$, *the other about a plane* (P) *passing through it, then they are symmetric about the line perpendicular to the plane at this point.*

Let A be a point of the given figure, A' the point symmetric to A about the center O, and A'' the point symmetric to A about the plane P. Denote by B the intersection point of the segment AA'' with the plane P. Draw the plane through the points A, A' and A''. This plane is perpendicular to the plane P since it contains the line AA'' perpendicular to this plane. In the plane $AA'A''$, draw the line l passing through the point O and parallel to AA''. This line is perpendicular to the plane P and to the line BO. Let C be the intersection point of the lines $A'A''$ and l.

In the triangle $AA'A''$, the segment BO is the midline parallel to $A'A''$. But $BO \perp l$, and hence $A'A'' \perp l$. Furthermore, since O is the midpoint of the segment AA', and the line l is parallel to AA'', we find that $A'C = CA''$. We conclude that the points A' and A'' are symmetric about the line l. Since the same holds true for any point A of the given figure, we conclude that the geometric locus of points A' symmetric to points of the given figure about the center O, and the geometric locus of points symmetric to points of the given figure about the plane P, are symmetric to each other about the line l.

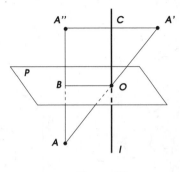

Figure 76

Corollaries. (1) *Two figures centrally symmetric to a given figure about two different centers are congruent to each other.* This follows from the lemma of §71, since figures centrally symmetric to the given one are homothetic to it with respect to two different centers and the same coefficient $k = -1$.

(2) *Two figures symmetric to a given figure about two different planes are congruent to each other.* Indeed, replace each figure, symmetric to the given one about a plane, by a congruent figure, namely by the figure symmetric to the given one about a center lying on the plane of symmetry. Then the problem reduces to the previous one about figures symmetric to the given one about different centers.

82. Axes of symmetry of higher orders. If a figure possesses an axis of symmetry of the 2nd order, it is superimposed onto itself by the rotation about this axis through the angle of 180°. It is possible however that a figure is superimposed onto itself after the rotation about a line through a certain angle smaller than 180°. Thus in the process of rotating the figure about this line, it occupies its original position several times. The number of times this happens (including the original position) is called the **order of symmetry**, and the line is called an axis of **symmetry of higher order**. For example, while

a regular triangular pyramid does not have axes of symmetry of the
2nd order, its altitude serves as an axis of symmetry of the 3rd order.
Indeed, after rotation through the angle of 120° about the altitude
(Figure 77), the pyramid occupies its original position. In the process
of rotation about this axis, the pyramid becomes superimposed onto
itself three times (after the rotation through the angles of 0°, 120°,
and 240°).

It is easy to see that any axis of symmetry of an even order is also
an axis of symmetry of the 2nd order. Regular pyramids, or regular
prisms, with n lateral faces are examples of solids with symmetries
of the nth order. The altitude (respectively the line connecting the
centers of the bases) is the axis.

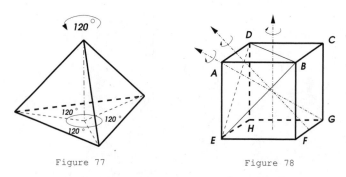

Figure 77   Figure 78

83. Symmetries of the cube. The intersection point of the
diagonals is the center of symmetry of the cube (Figure 78).

There are nine planes of symmetry: 6 diagonal planes (such as
$DBFH$) and three planes passing through the midpoints of each
quadruple of parallel edges.

The cube has nine axes of symmetry of the 2nd order: six lines
connecting the midpoints of opposite edges (e.g. of AD and FG),
and three lines connecting the centers of each pair of the opposite
faces. The latter lines are in fact axes of symmetry of the 4th order.
In addition, the cube has four axes of symmetry of the 3rd order,
namely its diagonals (e.g. AG). Indeed, the diagonal AG, obviously,
makes congruent angles with the edges AB, AD, and AE, and these
angles make the same (right) angles with each other. If we connect
the points B, D, and E, then we obtain a regular triangular pyramid,
$ABDE$, for which the diagonal AG is the altitude. When the cube is
rotated about this diagonal through the angle of 120°, the pyramid
returns to its original position. The same is true about the pyramid
$GHFC$, centrally symmetric to the pyramid $ABDE$. Thus, as the

result of this rotation, the whole cube returns to its original position. It is not hard to see that the cube does not have any other axes of symmetry.

Let us find out now, how many different ways of rotating the cube are there that preserve it as a whole. An axis of symmetry of the 2nd order gives only one such way (excluding the trivial rotation through $0°$). An axis of symmetry of the 3rd order gives two such ways, and of the 4th order three. Since the cube has six axes of symmetry of the 2nd order, four of the 3rd order, and three of the 4th order, we find that there are $6 \times 1 + 4 \times 2 + 3 \times 3 = 23$ ways, excluding the trivial one, to superimpose the cube onto itself by rotation.

It is not hard to see directly that all the 23 rotations are different from each other (e.g. by noting that some of the vertices A, B, C, etc. change their positions differently). Together with the trivial rotation (leaving the position of each vertex unchanged) they give 24 ways of superimposing the cube onto itself.

EXERCISES

123. Prove that the figure centrally symmetric to a line (or a plane), is a line (respectively a plane).

124. The same — for symmetry about a plane.

125. Prove that the figure symmetric to a dihedral angle about any plane is congruent to it.

126. Determine centers, axes, and planes of symmetry of the figure formed by a given line intersecting a given plane, but not perpendicular to it.

127. Determine centers, axes, and planes of symmetry for the figure consisting of two intersecting lines.

128.* Prove that a prism has a center of symmetry if and only if its base does.

129. Determine the number of planes of symmetry of a regular prism with n lateral faces.

130. Determine the number of planes of symmetry of a regular pyramid with n lateral faces.

131. Let three figures Φ, Φ', and Φ'' be symmetric: Φ and Φ' about a plane P, and Φ' and Φ'' about a plane Q perpendicular to P. Prove that Φ and Φ'' are symmetric about the intersection line of P and Q.

132. What can be said about the figures Φ and Φ'' of the previous problem if the planes P and Q make the angle: (a) $60°$? (b) $45°$?

133.* Prove that if a figure has two symmetry planes making an angle $180°/n$, then their intersection line is an axis of symmetry of the nth order.

134. Describe the cross section of a cube by the plane perpendicular to one of the diagonals at its midpoint.

135.* Show that the 24 ways of superimposing the cube onto itself correspond to 24 different ways (including the trivial one) of permuting its four diagonals.

5 Regular polyhedra

84. Definition. Let us call a polyhedral angle **regular** if all of its plane angles are congruent and all of its dihedral angles are congruent. A polyhedron is called **regular** if all of its faces are congruent regular polygons, and all of its polyhedral angles are regular and congruent. Thus a cube is a regular polyhedron. It follows from the definition, that in a regular polyhedron: all plane angles are congruent, all dihedral angles are congruent, and all edges are congruent.

85. Classification of regular polyhedra. Let us take into account that a convex polyhedral angle has at least three plane angles, and that their sum has to be smaller than $4d$ (§48).

Since in a regular triangle, every angle is $\frac{2}{3}d$, repeating it 3, 4, or 5 times, we obtain the angle sum smaller than $4d$, but repeating it 6 or more times, we get the angle sum equal to or greater than $4d$. Therefore convex polyhedral angles whose faces are angles of regular triangles can be of only three types: trihedral, tetrahedral, or pentahedral. Angles of squares and regular pentagons are respectively d and $\frac{6}{5}d$. Repeating these angles three times, we get the sums smaller than $4d$, but repeating them four or more times, we get the sums equal to or greater than $4d$. Therefore from angles of squares or regular pentagons, only trihedral convex angles can be formed. The angles of regular hexagons are $\frac{4}{3}d$, and of regular polygons with more than 6 sides even greater. The sum of three or more of such angles will be equal to or greater than $4d$. Therefore no convex polyhedral angles can be formed from such angles.

It follows that only the following five types of regular polyhedra can occur: those whose faces are regular triangles, meeting by three, four or five triangles at each vertex, or those whose faces are either squares, or regular pentagons, meeting by three faces at each vertex.

Regular polyhedra of each of the five types do exist and are often called **Platonic solids** after the Greek philosopher Plato. They are:

(i) **regular tetrahedron** whose surface is formed by 4 regular triangles (Figure 79);

(ii) **octahedron** whose surface is formed by 8 regular triangles (Figure 80);

(iii) **icosahedron** whose surface is formed by 20 regular triangles (Figure 81);

(iv) **cube** (or **hexahedron**) whose surface consists of 6 squares (Figure 82);

(v) **dodecahedron** whose surface is formed by 12 regular pentagons (Figure 83).

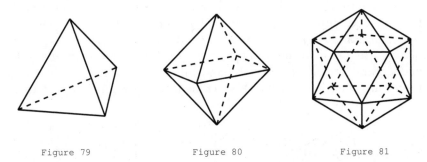

Figure 79   Figure 80   Figure 81

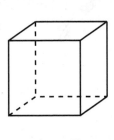
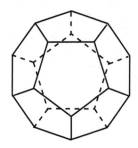

Figure 82   Figure 83

86. Constructions of Platonic solids. The above argument shows that regular polyhedra, if they exist, fall into five types, but it does not prove that regular polyhedra of each of the five types exist. In order to establish their existence it suffices to point out a construction of each of the five Platonic solids. In the case of the cube, which was defined as a rectangular parallelepiped all of whose three dimensions are congruent, such a construction is familiar to us. We will show here how each of the remaining four Platonic solids can be constructed from a cube.

A regular *tetrahedron* can be constructed by taking four of the eight vertices of a cube for the vertices of the tetrahedron as shown in Figure 84. Namely, pick any vertex A of the cube, and in the three square faces adjacent to this vertex, take the vertices B, C, and D opposite to A. The six edges connecting the vertices A, B, C, D pairwise are diagonals of the cube's faces (one diagonal in each face), and are therefore congruent. This shows that all faces of the tetrahedron are congruent regular triangles. Rotating the cube 120° about any of its diagonals (e.g the diagonal passing through the vertex A) will keep one of the vertices (A) of the tetrahedron in its place, but cyclically permute the edges, adjacent to it, and the other three vertices (e.g. move B into C, C into D, and D into B). The corresponding polyhedral angles become superimposed onto each other (the angle B onto the angle C, etc.) This shows that all polyhedral angles of the tetrahedron are congruent, and all dihedral angles (in each of them) are congruent. Thus the tetrahedron is a regular polyhedron.

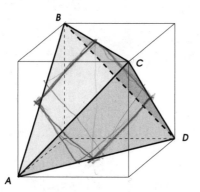

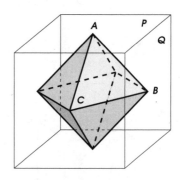

Figure 84   Figure 85

A regular *octahedron* can be constructed by taking the six centers of cube's faces (Figure 85) for the vertices. Each edge of the resulting polyhedron connects centers of two adjacent faces of the cube and, as easily computed, has the length $\frac{1}{\sqrt{2}}a$ where a denotes the cube's dimension. In particular, all edges have the same length, and hence all faces of the octahedron are congruent regular triangles. To prove that all dihedral and all polyhedral angles of the octahedron are congruent, we note that by rotating the cube (say, about axes passing through centers of opposite faces) one can move any face (e.g. P) of the cube onto any other (e.g. Q). Since the rotation preserves the cube, it also preserves the set of eight centers of the faces. Therefore the rotation preserves the octahedron as a whole, but moves the edges (CA to CB) and vertices (A to B). Thus the corresponding dihedral and polyhedral angles of the octahedron become superimposed.

A *dodecahedron* can be constructed by drawing 12 planes, one through each of the 12 edges of a cube (Figure 86), and choosing the slopes of these planes in such a way that the resulting polyhedron is regular. The fact that it is possible to achieve this is not obvious at all, and proving it will require some preparation.

Let us begin with examining a regular pentagon. All of its diagonals are congruent, and can be assumed to have the same length as the dimension of the cube. The angles of the pentagon contain $108°$ each. If we place two copies of the pentagon in one plane so that they have an edge in common, the angles at the common vertices will add up to $216°$ which is smaller by $144°$ than the full angle. Therefore we can rotate the two pentagons in space about their common edge (AB, Figure 87), so that their planes form a dihedral angle, until the angle CAF decreases from $144°$ to $108°$. Since the figure formed by the two regular pentagons in space is symmetric about the plane perpendicular to the edge AB at the midpoint, the angle DBE symmetric to the angle CAF will also contain $108°$. This means that two more regular pentagons congruent to the original ones can be attached, one to the edges FA and AC (shown in Figure 87 as $GCAFH$), the other to the edges EB and BD. If we now draw the diagonals CD, DE, EF, and FC in these pentagons, they will form a square. Indeed, $CD \| EF$ (since these diagonals are parallel to the common side AB of the pentagons) and thus $CDEF$ is a rhombus, and $\angle FCD = \angle EDC$ (as angles symmetric about the plane perpendicular to the line AB at the midpoint).

Let us now examine the tent-like polyhedron $ABCDEF$ shaded in Figure 87. From the vertex A, drop the perpendicular AO to its base $CDEF$, then draw two slants: AM and AN perpendicular respectively to CD and FC, and finally draw their projections OM and ON to the base. Then, by the theorem of the three perpendiculars (§28), $OM \perp CD$, $ON \perp FC$, and therefore $\angle AMO$ and $\angle ANO$ are linear angles of the dihedral angles formed by the base $CDEF$ with the lateral faces $CABD$ and AFC respectively.

Since the base of the tent-like polyhedron is a square, we can attach polyhedra congruent to it, to each of the faces of the cube as shown in Figure 86. We claim that in the resulting polyhedron, the faces (triangles and quadrilaterals) of the attached tent-line polyhedra will agree in their slopes and thus form regular pentagons.

In order to show that the slopes agree, it suffices to check that the dihedral angle formed by the lateral face $ABCD$ and the base $CDEF$ is congruent to the dihedral angle formed by the extension $FHGC$ of the triangle FAC and the face P of the cube adjacent to the base $CDEB$. Since the plane P is perpendicular to the base, it suffices to check instead that the dihedral angles, formed by the faces $ABCD$ and FAC with the same plane $CDEF$, add up to $90°$, i.e. that $\angle AMO + \angle ANO = 90°$. For this, we will compute $\cos(\angle AMO) = OM : AM$ and $\cos(\angle ANO) = ON : AN$, and show that they are legs of a right triangle with the hypotenuse equal to 1:

$$\left(\frac{OM}{AM}\right)^2 + \left(\frac{ON}{AN}\right)^2 = 1.$$

Note that $\angle ACM = 72°$, and $\angle ACN = 36°$, so we have:

$$OM = NC = AC \cdot \cos 36°, \quad AM = AC \cdot \sin 72°,$$
$$ON = MC = AC \cdot \cos 72°, \quad AN = AC \cdot \sin 36°.$$

As we found in Book I, §223, in an isosceles triangle with the angle at the vertex $36°$ (and hence the angles $72°$ at the base), the ratio of the base to the lateral side is equal to the golden mean $(\sqrt{5} - 1)/2$. From the geometry of this triangle, we find:

$$\cos 72° = \frac{\sqrt{5} - 1}{4}, \quad \cos 36° = 1 - 2\cos^2 72° = \frac{\sqrt{5} + 1}{4}.$$

Using the identity $\cos^2 \alpha + \sin^2 \alpha = 1$, we compute:

$$\cos^2 72° = \frac{3 - \sqrt{5}}{8}, \quad \sin^2 72° = \frac{5 + \sqrt{5}}{8},$$
$$\cos^2 36° = \frac{3 + \sqrt{5}}{8}, \quad \sin^2 36° = \frac{5 - \sqrt{5}}{8}.$$

Therefore

$$\left(\frac{OM}{AM}\right)^2 + \left(\frac{ON}{AN}\right)^2 = \frac{\cos^2 36°}{\sin^2 72°} + \frac{\cos^2 72°}{\sin^2 36°}$$
$$= \frac{3 + \sqrt{5}}{5 + \sqrt{5}} + \frac{3 - \sqrt{5}}{5 - \sqrt{5}} = \frac{(3 + \sqrt{5})(5 - \sqrt{5}) + (3 - \sqrt{5})(5 + \sqrt{5})}{(5 + \sqrt{5})(5 - \sqrt{5})}$$
$$= \frac{10 + 2\sqrt{5} + 10 - 2\sqrt{5}}{20} = \frac{20}{20} = 1.$$

As a by-product, we have computed the ratio $OM : AM$, i.e. the sine of the angle OAM, which is a half of the linear angle of the dihedral angle AB. Note that we used only the fact that plane angles of the trihedral angle A contain $108°$ each. This shows that all trihedral angles with this property have congruent dihedral angles and are therefore congruent to each other (§50). Thus the constructed polyhedron with 12 regular pentagonal faces is regular.

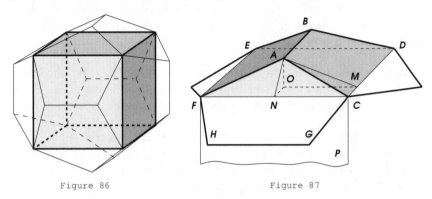

Figure 86   Figure 87

Once the existence of the dodecahedron is established, a regular *icosahedron* can be constructed by taking the centers of 12 faces of the dodecahedron for the vertices.

87. Theorem. *Any regular polyhedron is similar to one of the five Platonic solids.*

In §85, we proved that any regular polyhedron R falls into the same type as one of the five Platonic solids P. Replace now the polyhedron R with a polyhedron Q, homothetic to it and such that the edges of Q have the same length as the edges of P, and prove that Q is congruent to P. For this we need to establish first that Q and P have congruent polyhedral angles. We know that these polyhedral angles are regular and have the same number of congruent plane angles. Let the regular polyhedral angle S be one them, with n plane angles α (see Figure 88, where $n = 5$). It is easy to see that S has an axis of symmetry of the nth order. It can be located as the intersection line SO of two planes of symmetry, e.g. of the bisector plane ASO of the dihedral angle, and of the plane HSO passing through the bisector SH of the plane angle ASE and perpendicular to its plane. Draw the plane perpendicular to the axis of symmetry and passing through any point O on it in the interior of the polyhedral angle S. Then the cross section of the polyhedral angle by this plane will be a regular n-gon $ABCDE$. In the faces of the dihedral angle

SB, drop perpendiculars AG and CG to the edge SB from the vertices A and C of the n-gon, and consider the isosceles triangle AGC. The length of its lateral side AG is determined by the side AB of the n-gon and by $\angle SBA = (180° - \alpha)/2$. The base AC is a diagonal of the regular n-gon and is determined by its side AB. Thus the angle AGC is determined by the number n of the plane angles and their measure α. But the angle AGC is the linear angle of the dihedral angle SB. This proves that *regular polyhedral angles with the same number and measure of their plane angles* have congruent dihedral angles, and therefore *are congruent to each other*.

Using this, we can pick one vertex in each of the polyhedra Q and P and superimpose their polyhedral angles at this vertex. Since the edges of these polyhedra are congruent, the adjacent vertices will also coincide. Since all dihedral angles of both polyhedra are congruent to each other, the polyhedral angles at these adjacent vertices also become superimposed. Examining the edges adjacent to these vertices, and proceeding this way to other vertices, we conclude that the polyhedra Q and P are superimposed.

88. Remark. We accepted a very demanding definition of regular polyhedra and found that, up to scale, there are only five such polyhedra. One may ask if the same conclusion can be derived from milder requirements of regularity. It turns out that the answer is "yes": in order to conclude that a polyhedron is regular, it suffices to require that *all of the faces are congruent regular polygons and polyhedral angles are congruent* (but assume nothing about dihedral angles). In fact, many attempts to relax the definition even further lead to mistakes. First, merely assuming that all faces are congruent regular polygons is not enough (to construct a counterexample, attach two congruent regular tetrahedra to each other by their bases). Next, the class of polyhedra, all of whose polyhedral angles are congruent and faces regular, includes regular prisms with square lateral sides. This class was first systematically explored by a German mathematician and astronomer **Johannes Kepler**. In 1619, he found that in addition to the prisms, it also includes **antiprisms** (Figure 89), and 15 **Archimedean solids** (13, if symmetric polyhedra are not distinguished), which were described in the 4th century A.D. by a Greek mathematician **Pappus** and attributed by him to Archimedes. Although regularly shaped solids of various kinds were thoroughly studied and classified in the 20th century, the ancient symmetry patterns of the five Platonic solids still play the most fundamental role in modern mathematics and physics.

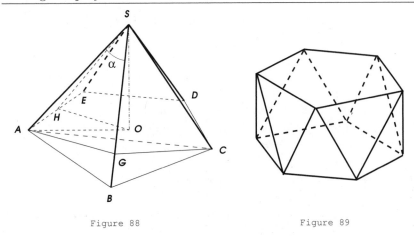

Figure 88   Figure 89

EXERCISES

136. Describe those pyramids all of whose edges are congruent.

137. Check that the numbers of vertices, edges, and faces of a cube are equal respectively to the numbers of faces, edges and vertices of an octahedron.

138. The same — for icosahedron and dodecahedron. Is there a way to establish this result without counting?

139. Prove that the polyhedron whose vertices are centers of faces of a tetrahedron is a tetrahedron again.

140.* Prove that the polyhedron whose vertices are centers of faces of an octahedron (or icosahedron) is a cube (respectively a dodecahedron).

141. Which of the five Platonic solids have a center of symmetry?

142. Describe all ways to superimpose a regular tetrahedron onto itself by rotations, and show that there are 12 such rotations (including the trivial one).

143. Show that each of the 12 rotations of a regular tetrahedron permutes the four vertices, and that to different rotations there correspond different permutations of the set of vertices.

144. How many planes of symmetry does a regular tetrahedron have?

145.* Realize all permutations of the four vertices of a regular tetrahedron by reflections in symmetry planes and rotations.

146. Prove that an octahedron has as many planes of symmetry and axes of symmetry of each order as a cube does.

147. The same — about icosahedron and dodecahedron.

148. Show that a cube has nine planes of symmetry.

149. Locate all 15 planes of symmetry of an icosahedron.

150.* Find all axes of symmetry (of any order) of an icosahedron, and show that there are in total 60 ways (including the trivial one) to superimpose the icosahedron onto itself by rotation.

151. Describe cross sections of the icosahedron or dodecahedron by the plane passing through the center and perpendicular to one of the axes of symmetry.

152. Do there exist six lines passing through the same point and making congruent angles to each other?

153. Show that diagonals of a dodecahedron's faces are edges of five cubes inscribed into the dodecahedron.

154.* Show that each of the 60 rotations of a dodecahedron permutes the five cubes inscribed into it, and that to different rotations there correspond different permutations of the set of five cubes.

155. Give an accurate construction of an n-gonal **antiprism** (referring to Figure 89 as an example with $n = 5$), a polyhedron which has two parallel regular n-gons as bases, $2n$ regular triangles as lateral faces, and all of whose polyhedral angles are congruent. Prove that when $n = 3$, the antiprism is an octahedron.
Hint: See the front cover.

156. Cut an icosahedron into two regular pyramids and an antiprism.

157.* Find and compare the numbers of planes and axes of symmetry (of each order) of: (a) a regular n-gon in space, (b) the polyhedron obtained from two copies of a regular n-gonal pyramid attached to each other by their bases, (c) a regular n-gonal prism, (d) an n-gonal antiprism.

158. Compute volumes of regular tetrahedron and octahedron with the edge a.

159.* Prove that the volume of an icosahedron with the edge a is equal to $\frac{5}{12}(3 + \sqrt{5})a^3$.

160.* Prove that the volume of a dodecahedron with the edge a is equal to $\frac{1}{4}(15 + 7\sqrt{5})a^3$.
Hint: Represent the dodecahedron as a cube with congruent "tent-like" solids attached to each of its six faces, and compute the volume of the solid first.

Chapter 3

ROUND SOLIDS

1 Cylinders and cones

89. Surfaces of revolution. A **surface of revolution** is the surface obtained by rotating any curve (MN, Figure 90), called a **generatrix** (or **generator**) about a fixed line (AB), called the **axis of revolution**.

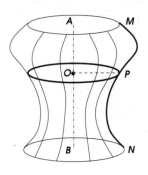

Figure 90

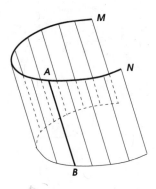

Figure 91

On the generatrix, take any point P and drop from it the perpendicular PO to the axis. Obviously, in the process of rotation of the generatrix about the axis, the angle APO, the length of the perpendicular, and the position of its foot O remain unchanged. Therefore each point of the generatrix describes a circle, the plane of which is perpendicular to the axis of revolution, and the center of which is the intersection of this plane with the axis.

Thus, *the cross section of a surface of revolution by a plane perpendicular to the axis consists of one or several circles.*

Any plane containing the axis of revolution is called **meridional**, and the cross section of the surface by this plane a **meridian**. All meridians of a given surface of revolution are congruent to each other, because in the process of revolution each of them assumes the positions of every other meridian.

90. Cylindrical surfaces. A **cylindrical surface** is the surface swept by a line (AB, Figure 91) moving in space so that it remains parallel to a given direction and intersects a given curve (MN). The line AB is called the **generatrix** (or **generator**), and the curve MN the **directrix** of the cylindrical surface.

91. Cylinders. A **cylinder** is a solid bounded by a cylindrical surface and two parallel planes (Figure 92) intersecting the generatrices.[1] The part of the cylindrical surface contained between the planes is called the **lateral surface**, and the parts of the planes cut out by this surface **bases** of the cylinder. A perpendicular dropped from any point of one base to the plane of the other is called an **altitude** of the cylinder. A cylinder is called **right**, if its generatrices are perpendicular to the bases, and **oblique** otherwise.

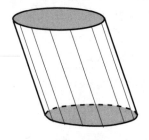
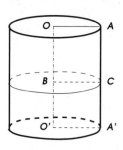

Figure 92   Figure 93

A right cylinder whose bases are disks is called a **right circular cylinder** (Figure 93). Such a cylinder can be considered as a solid obtained by rotating a rectangle ($OAA'O'$) about one of its sides (OO'). The opposite side (AA') describes then the lateral surface, and the other two sides the bases. A segment BC (see Figure 93) parallel to OA also describes a disk whose plane is perpendicular to the axis OO'.

---

[1] *Generatrices* is used as the plural for *generatrix*.

Thus, *cross sections of a right circular cylinder by planes parallel to the bases are disks.*

In our elementary exposition, we will consider only right circular cylinders, and for the sake of brevity refer to them simply as *cylinders*. Sometimes we will deal with prisms whose bases are polygons inscribed into the bases of a cylinder, or circumscribed about them, and the altitudes are congruent to the altitude of the cylinder. We will call such prisms **inscribed** into (respectively **circumscribed** about) the cylinder.

92. Conical surfaces. A **conical surface** is the surface obtained by moving a line (AB, Figure 94) so that it passes through a fixed point (S) and intersects a given curve (MN). The line AB is called a **generatrix**, the curve MN the **directrix**, and the point S the **vertex** of the conical surface.

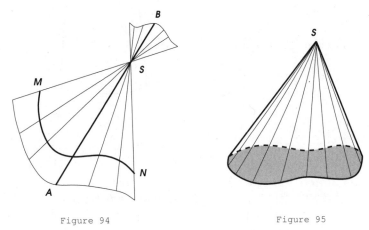

Figure 94   Figure 95

93. Cones. A **cone** is a solid enclosed between a conical surface and a plane intersecting all generatrices on one side of the vertex (Figure 95). The part of the conical surface enclosed between the vertex and the plane is called the **lateral surface**, and the part of the plane cut out by the conical surface the **base** of the cone. The perpendicular dropped from the vertex to the plane of the base is called the **altitude** of the cone.

A cone is called **right circular** if the base is a disk, and the altitude passes through its center (Figure 96). Such a cone can be obtained by rotating a right triangle (SOA) about one of its legs (SO). Then the other leg (OA) describes the base, and the hypotenuse (SA) the lateral surface of the cone. A segment BC (Figure 96) parallel to OA also describes a disk perpendicular to the axis SO.

Thus, *cross sections of a right circular cone by planes parallel to the base are disks.*

We will consider only right circular cones and refer to them simply as *cones* for the sake of brevity. Sometimes we will consider pyramids whose vertices coincide with the vertex of a given cone, and bases are inscribed into, or circumscribed about its base. We will call such pyramids **inscribed** into the cone, and respectively **circumscribed** about it.

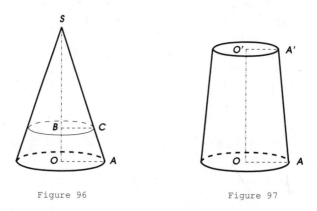

Figure 96   Figure 97

94. Conical frusta. A **conical frustum** is the part of a cone enclosed between the base and a cross section parallel to it. The parallel disks (the base of the cone, and the cross section) are called **bases** of the conical frustum.

A conical frustum (Figure 97) can be obtained by rotation about an axis OO', of a trapezoid $OAA'O'$ whose lateral side OO' is perpendicular to the bases.

95. Surface area of cones and cylinders. The lateral surface of a cylinder or cone is *curved*, i.e. no part of it can be superimposed onto a plane. Therefore we need to *define* what is meant by area of such surfaces when it is expressed in the units of area of plane figures. We will accept the following definitions.

(1) *For the* **lateral surface area of a cylinder,** *we take the limit to which the lateral surface area of a regular prism inscribed into the cylinder tends as the number of its lateral faces increases indefinitely* (and hence the area of each lateral face tends to zero).

(2) *For the* **lateral surface area of a cone,** (or **conical frustum**) *we take the limit to which the lateral surface area of an inscribed regular pyramid* (or *regular pyramidal frustum*) *tends as the number of its lateral faces increases indefinitely* (and hence the area of each lateral face tends to zero).

96. Theorem. *The lateral surface area of a cylinder is equal to the product of the circumference of the base and an altitude.*

Into a cylinder (Figure 98), inscribe any regular prism. Denote by p and h the perimeter of the base and the altitude of the prism respectively. Then the lateral surface area of the prism is expressed by the product $p \cdot h$. Suppose now that the number of lateral faces of the prism increases indefinitely. Then the perimeter p tends to a limit, taken to be the circumference c of the cylinder's base, and the altitude h remains unchanged. Therefore the lateral surface area $p \cdot h$ of the prism tends to the limit $c \cdot h$. By definition (1), this limit is taken to be the lateral surface area s of the cylinder. Therefore

$$s = c \cdot h.$$

Figure 98

Corollaries. (1) If r denotes the radius of the cylinder's base, then $c = 2\pi r$, and hence the lateral surface area of the cylinder is expressed by the formula:

$$s = 2\pi r h.$$

(2) To obtain the **total surface area** of the cylinder, it suffices to add the lateral surface area and the areas of the two bases. Thus, if t denotes the total area of the cylinder, we have:

$$t = 2\pi r h + \pi r^2 + \pi r^2 = 2\pi r (h + r).$$

97. Theorem. *The lateral surface area of a cone is equal to the product of the circumference of the base and a half of a generatrix.*

Into a cone (Figure 99), inscribe any regular pyramid, and denote by p and a the numbers expressing the perimeter of the base and the length of the apothem of this pyramid. Then (§60) the lateral surface area of the pyramid is expressed as $\frac{1}{2}p \cdot a$. Suppose now that the number of the lateral faces of the pyramid increases indefinitely. Then the perimeter p tends to a limit, taken for the circumference c of the cone's base, and the apothem a tends to the generatrix l of the cone. (Indeed, the generatrix SA is the hypotenuse of the right triangle SAL and is greater than the leg SL which is an apothem of the pyramid. The other leg AL is a half of the side of the regular polygon in the base, and tends to zero as the number of sides increases indefinitely. Since $SA - SL < AL$, we conclude that a tends to l.) Therefore the lateral surface area $\frac{1}{2}p \cdot a$ of the pyramid tends to the limit $\frac{1}{2}c \cdot l$. By definition (2) the limit is taken to be the lateral surface area s of the cone. Thus

$$s = c \cdot l/2.$$

Figure 99

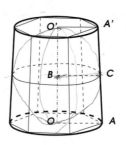

Figure 100

Corollaries. (1) Since $c = 2\pi r$, where r is the radius of the base, the lateral surface area of the cone is expressed by the formula:

$$s = \frac{1}{2} \cdot 2\pi r \cdot l = \pi r l.$$

(2) The **total surface area** of the cone is obtained from the lateral one by adding the area of the base. If t denotes the total area, we have:

$$t = \pi r l + \pi r^2 = \pi r (l + r).$$

98. Theorem. *The lateral surface area of a conical frustum is equal to the product of a generatrix and half the sum of the circumferences of the bases.*

Into a conical frustum (Figure 100), inscribe any regular pyramidal frustum. Denote by p and p' perimeters of the lower and upper bases, and by a the length of an apothem. Then (§60) the lateral surface area of the pyramidal frustum is equal to $\frac{1}{2}(p + p')a$. As the number of lateral faces increases indefinitely, the perimeters p and p' tend to the limits taken for the circumferences c and c' of the bases, and the apothem a tends to the generatrix l of the conical frustum. Therefore the lateral surface area of the pyramidal frustum tends to a limit equal to $\frac{1}{2}(c + c')l$. By definition (2), this limit is taken for the lateral surface area s of the conical frustum, i.e.

$$s = \frac{1}{2}(c + c')l.$$

99. Corollaries. (1) If r and r' denote the radii of the lower and upper bases, then the lateral surface area of a conical frustum is expressed by the formula:

$$s = \frac{1}{2}(2\pi r + 2\pi r')l = \pi(r + r')l.$$

(2) Considering the conical frustum (Figure 100) as a solid obtained by rotation of the trapezoid $OAA'O'$ about the axis OO', draw the midline BC of the trapezoid. We have:

$$BC = \frac{1}{2}(OA + O'A') = \frac{1}{2}(r + r'), \text{ and hence } r + r' = 2BC.$$

Therefore $s = 2\pi \cdot BC \cdot l$, i.e. *the lateral surface area of a conical frustum is equal to the product of a generatrix and the circumference of the middle cross section.*

(3) The **total surface area** of a conical frustum is

$$t = \pi(r^2 + r'^{\,2} + rl + r'l).$$

100. Nets of cylinders and cones. Into a cylinder (Figure 101), inscribe any regular prism, and then imagine that the lateral surface of the prism is cut along a lateral edge. Rotating lateral faces about the edges one can *develop* the surface (without breaking it or distorting the faces) into a plane figure. The resulting figure is called the **net** (or **development**) of the lateral surface of the prism. The net is a rectangle $KLMN$ consisting of as many smaller rectangles as there are lateral faces of the prism. The base MN of the rectangle is congruent to the perimeter of the base, and the altitude KN to the altitude of the prism.

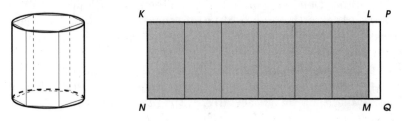

Figure 101

Imagine now that the number of lateral faces of the prism increases indefinitely. Then the net of its lateral surface becomes longer and longer, and in the limit, tends to a certain rectangle $KPQN$, such that the altitude and base are congruent respectively to the altitude of the cylinder and the circumference of its base. This rectangle is called the **net** (or **development**) of the lateral surface **of the cylinder.**

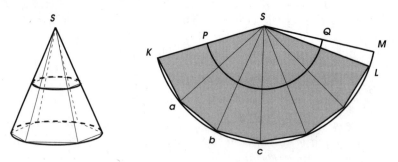

Figure 102

Similarly, into a cone (Figure 102), inscribe any regular pyramid. We can cut its lateral surface along an edge and then, rotating lateral faces about the edges, develop it to the plane into a **net** shaped as a polygonal sector SKL, which consists of as many isosceles triangles as there are lateral faces in the pyramid. The segments $SK, Sa, Sb, \ldots$ are congruent to lateral edges of the pyramid (or to generatrices of the cone), and the length of the broken line $Kab\ldots L$

is equal to the perimeter of the pyramid's base. As the number of lateral faces increases indefinitely, the net tends to the sector SKM whose radius SK is congruent to a generatrix of the cone, and the length of the arc KM is equal to the circumference of the cone's base. This sector is called the **net** of the lateral surface **of the cone.**

One can similarly construct the **net** of the lateral surface **of a conical frustum** (Figure 102) as the part $PKMQ$ of an annulus. It is easy to see that the lateral surface area of a cylinder, cone, or conical frustum is equal to the area of the corresponding net.

101. Volumes of cylinders and cones.

Definitions. (1) *For the* **volume of a cylinder,** *we take the limit to which the volume of a regular prism inscribed into the cylinder tends as the number of lateral faces of the prism increases indefinitely.*

(2) *For the* **volume of a cone** (or **conical frustum**), *we take the limit to which the volume of an inscribed regular pyramid* (or *regular pyramidal frustum) tends as the number of lateral faces increases indefinitely.*

Theorems. (1) ***The volume of a cylinder is equal to the product of the area of the base and the altitude.***

(2) ***The volume of a cone is equal to the product of the area of the base and a third of the altitude.***

Into a cylinder, inscribe any regular prism, and into a cone any regular pyramid. Then, if we denote by B the area of the base of the prism or pyramid, their altitude by h, and the volume by V, then we find (§65 and §68):

$$\text{for prisms } V = Bh; \quad \text{for pyramids } V = \frac{1}{3}Bh.$$

Imagine now that the number of lateral faces of the prism or pyramid increases indefinitely. Then B tends to a limit equal to the area b of the base of the cylinder or cone, and the altitude will remain unchanged. Therefore the volume V will tend to the limit bh in the case of prisms, and $\frac{1}{3}bh$ in the case of pyramids. Therefore the volume v of the cylinder or cone is given by the formula:

$$\text{for the cylinder } v = bh; \quad \text{for the cone } v = \frac{1}{3}bh.$$

Corollary. If r denotes the radius of the base of a cylinder or cone, then $b = \pi r^2$, and hence *for the volume of the cylinder we have* $v = \pi r^2 h$, *and for the volume of the cone* $v = \pi r^2 h/3$.

102. Similar cones and cylinders. According to the general
definition of similar figures (§75), a solid similar to a cone (or cylinder) is congruent to the solid homothetic to this cone (respectively
cylinder).

Consider the cone (Figure 103) obtained by rotating a right triangle SOA about the axis SO, and let $SO'A'$ be the triangle homothetic to $\triangle SOA$ with respect to the center S. Rotating $\triangle SO'A'$
about the axis SO', we obtain a cone homothetic to the given one.
Since any solid similar to the given cone must be congruent to one
of these cones (with an appropriate choice of the homothety coefficient), we conclude that *a figure similar to a cone is a cone*, and that
*two cones are similar if they are obtained by rotating similar right
triangles about homologous legs.*

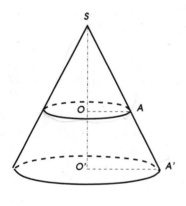

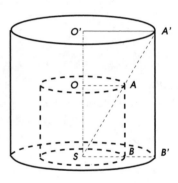

Figure 103   Figure 104

Likewise, considering the cylinder (Figure 104) formed by rotating a rectangle $SOAB$ about its side SO and applying a homothety
with the center S, we obtain the cylinder formed by rotating the rectangle $SO'A'B'$, homothetic to the given one, about the side SO'. We
conclude from this that *a solid similar to a cylinder is a cylinder*,
and that *two cylinders are similar if they are obtained by rotating
similar rectangles about homologous sides.*

Let us denote by h and h' the altitudes SO and SO' (Figures
103 and 104) of the similar cones or cylinders, by r and r' the radii
OA and OA' of their bases, and by l and l' the generatrices SA and
SA' of the similar cones (Figure 103). From similarity of the right
triangles SOA and $SO'A'$ (or rectangles $SOAB$ and $SO'A'B'$), we

find:

$$\frac{r}{r'} = \frac{h}{h'}, \quad \text{and} \quad \frac{r}{r'} = \frac{l}{l'}.$$

Applying properties of equal ratios, we derive:

$$\frac{r+h}{r'+h'} = \frac{r}{r'}, \quad \text{and} \quad \frac{r+l}{r'+l'} = \frac{r}{r'}.$$

Using these proportions we obtain the following results.

103. Theorem. *Lateral and total surface areas of similar cones or cylinders are proportional to the squares of the radii or altitudes, and their volumes are proportional to the cubes of the radii or altitudes.*

Let s, t, and v be respectively: the lateral surface, total surface, and volume of one cone or cylinder, and s', t', and v' be those of the other solid similar to the first one. For the cylinders, we have:

$$\frac{s}{s'} = \frac{2\pi r h}{2\pi r' h'} = \frac{r}{r'}\frac{h}{h'} = \frac{r^2}{r'^{\,2}} = \frac{h^2}{h'^{\,2}};$$

$$\frac{t}{t'} = \frac{2\pi r(r+h)}{2\pi r'(r'+h')} = \frac{r}{r'}\frac{r+h}{r'+h'} = \frac{r^2}{r'^{\,2}} = \frac{h^2}{h'^{\,2}};$$

$$\frac{v}{v'} = \frac{\pi r^2 h}{\pi r'^{\,2} h'} = \left(\frac{r}{r'}\right)^2 \frac{h}{h'} = \frac{r^3}{r'^{\,3}} = \frac{h^3}{h'^{\,3}}.$$

For the cones, we have:

$$\frac{s}{s'} = \frac{\pi r l}{\pi r' l'} = \frac{r}{r'}\frac{l}{l'} = \frac{r^2}{r'^{\,2}} = \frac{h^2}{h'^{\,2}};$$

$$\frac{t}{t'} = \frac{\pi r(r+l)}{\pi r'(r'+l')} = \frac{r}{r'}\frac{r+l}{r'+l'} = \frac{r^2}{r'^{\,2}} = \frac{h^2}{h'^{\,2}};$$

$$\frac{v}{v'} = \frac{\frac{1}{3}\pi r^2 h}{\frac{1}{3}\pi r'^{\,2} h'} = \left(\frac{r}{r'}\right)^2 \frac{h}{h'} = \frac{r^3}{r'^{\,3}} = \frac{h^3}{h'^{\,3}}.$$

EXERCISES

161. Show that the surface obtained by translating a curve in the direction of a given line is cylindrical.

162. Find all planes, axes, and centers of symmetry of a (right circular) cylinder.

163. Prove that an oblique cylinder (§91) is equivalent to the right cylinder with the same generatrix and the base congruent to the perpendicular cross section of the oblique cylinder.

164. Use Cavalieri's principle to prove that an oblique cylinder is equivalent to a right cylinder with the same base and the generatrix congruent to the altitude of the oblique cylinder.

165. A cross section of a (right circular) cylinder, not intersecting the bases, makes the angle α with them. Compute the area of the cross section given the radius r of the base.

166. Find a triangular pyramid which admits a square as a net, and compute its volume, assuming that the side of the square is a.

167. On the surface of a regular tetrahedron, find the shortest path between the midpoints of two opposite edges.

168. Can a unit cube be wrapped into a square piece of paper with sides 3?

169. The **axial cross section** (i.e. the cross section passing through the axis) of a cone has the angle of $60°$ at the vertex. Compute the angle at the vertex of the cone's net.

170. Prove that the plane passing through a generatrix of a cone (resp. cylinder) and perpendicular to the plane of axial cross section passing through this generatrix does not have other common points with the cone (resp. cylinder).
Remark: This plane is called **tangent** to the cone (resp. cylinder).

171. Can a pair of cones with a common vertex have: (a) a common tangent plane? (b) infinitely many common tangent planes?

172. Two cones with a common vertex which have a common generatrix and the same tangent plane passing through it are called **tangent**. Prove that two tangent cones have a common symmetry plane.

173. The lateral surface area of a cylinder is equal to half of the total surface area. Compute the ratio of the altitude to the diameter of the base.

174. Generatrices of a cone make the angle of $60°$ with the base. Compute the ratio of the lateral surface area to the area of the base.

175. Compute the volume and the lateral surface area of a conical frustum that has the generatrix 15 cm long, and the radii of the bases 18 cm and 27 cm.

176. In a cone of volume V, two cross sections parallel to the base are drawn dividing the altitude into three congruent parts. Compute the volume of the conical frustum enclosed between these cross sections.

177. Compute the volume and the total surface area of the solid obtained by rotating a regular triangle with the edge a about the axis passing through its vertex and parallel to the opposite side.

178. Compute the volume and the total surface area of the solid obtained by rotating a square with the side a about the axis passing through one of the vertices and parallel to one of the diagonals.

179. Compute the total surface area of a solid obtained by rotating a rhombus of the area A about one of its sides.

180. Compute the volume and the total surface area of the solid obtained by rotating a regular hexagon with the side a about one of its sides.

181. The lateral surface area of a cone is twice the area of the base, and the area of the cross section by the plane containing the axis is A. Compute the volume of the cone.

182. Compute the volume of a cone if the radius of the base is r and the angle at the vertex of the cone's net is: (a) 90°, (b) 120°, (c) 60°.

183. Prove that the volume of a cone is equal to one third of the product of the lateral surface area and the distance from the center of the base to a generatrix.

184.⋆ Prove that the volume of a conical frustum is equal to the sum of the volumes of three cones, all having the same altitude as the conical frustum, and whose bases are respectively: the lower base of the frustum, the upper base of the frustum, and a disk with the area equal to the geometric mean between the areas of the other two bases.

185.⋆ Compute the ratio of volumes of two solids obtained by dividing a cone by the plane passing through the vertex and intersecting the base along a chord congruent to the radius.

186.⋆ Two perpendicular generatrices divide the lateral surface area of a cone in the ratio 2 : 1. Compute the volume of the cone if the radius of its base is r.

187.⋆ Find out which of the cross sections, passing through the vertex of a cone, has the maximal area, and prove that it is the axial cross section if and only if the radius of the base does not exceed the altitude of the cone.

188. Compute the volume and lateral surface area of the cylinder whose bases are circumscribed about two faces of a given octahedron with the edge a.

189.⋆ Four congruent cones with a common vertex are pairwise tangent to each other. Compute the ratio of the altitude of each cone to the generatrix.

2   The ball

104. Balls and spheres.

Definitions. A solid obtained by rotating a half-disk about the diameter is called a **ball**, and the surface swept by the semicircle is called a **spherical surface** or simply **sphere**. One can also say that a sphere is the geometric locus of points lying at a specified distance from a fixed point (called the **center** of the sphere and the ball).

The segment connecting the center with any point on the sphere is called a **radius**, and the segment connecting two points on the sphere and passing through the center is called a **diameter** of the ball. All radii of the same ball are congruent to each other, and to a half of a diameter.

Two balls of the same radius are congruent, because they become superimposed when their centers are placed at the same point.

105. Cross sections of a ball.

Theorem. *Any cross section of a ball by a plane is a disk.*

Suppose at first that the plane of the cross section (P, Figure 105) passes through the center O of the ball. All points of the intersection curve with the spherical surface are equidistant from the center. Therefore the cross section is a disk centered at the point O.

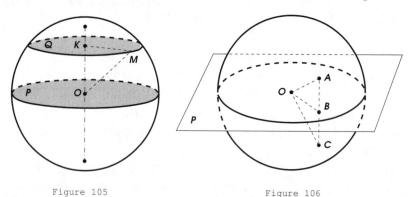

Figure 105   Figure 106

Consider now the case when the plane of the cross section (Q, Figure 105) does not pass through the center. From the center O, drop the perpendicular OK to the plane Q, and take any point M on the intersection of the plane with the sphere. Connecting M with O and K we obtain a right triangle OKM and find:

$$MK = \sqrt{OM^2 - OK^2}. \tag{$*$}$$

As the position of the point M varies, the lengths of the segments OM and OK do not change, and therefore the distance MK remains constant. Thus the cross section of the sphere lies on a circle, and the point K is its center. It follows from (∗) that, conversely, every point M of this circle lies on the sphere.

Corollaries. Let R and r denote the lengths of the radii of a ball and a cross section, and d be the distance from the center to the plane of the cross section. Then the equality (∗) assumes the form $r = \sqrt{R^2 - d^2}$. It follows that:

(1) *The greatest radius of the cross section is obtained if $d = 0$, i.e. if the plane passes through the center of the ball.* Then $r = R$. The circle obtained as such a cross section of the sphere is called a **great circle**.

(2) *The smallest radius of the cross section is obtained when $d = R$.* In this case, $r = 0$, i.e. the disk turns into a point.

(3) *Cross sections equidistant from the center are congruent.*

(4) *Out of two cross sections, the one that is closer to the center of the ball has the greater radius.*

106. Great circles.

Theorem. *Any plane* (P, Figure 106) *passing through the center of a ball divides its surface into two symmetric and congruent parts* (called **hemispheres**).

On the spherical surface, consider any point A, and let AB be the perpendicular dropped from the point A to the plane P. Extend the line AB past the point B until it meets the spherical surface at a point C. Connecting A, B and C with the center O, we obtain two congruent right triangles ABO and CBO. (They have a common leg BO and hypotenuses AO and CO congruent as radii of the ball.) Therefore $AB = BC$, and hence to each point A of the spherical surface, there corresponds another point C of the same surface symmetric to the point A about the plane P. Thus the two hemispheres into which the plane P divides the sphere are symmetric.

The hemispheres are not only symmetric but also congruent, since by cutting the ball along the plane P and rotating one of the parts through 180° about any diameter lying in the plane P we will superimpose the first hemisphere onto the second.

Theorem. *Through any two points of a spherical surface, other than the endpoints of the same diameter, one can draw a great circle, and such a great circle is unique.*

On a spherical surface with the center O (Figure 107), let two point A and B be given not lying on the same line with the point O. Then through the points A, B, and O, a unique plane can be drawn. This plane, passing through the center O, intersects the sphere along a great circle containing the points A and B.

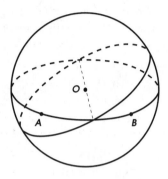

Figure 107

Another great circle passing through A and B cannot exist. Indeed, any great circle is obtained as a cross section of the sphere by a plane passing through the center O. If another great circle were passing through A and B, we would have two distinct planes passing through the same three points A, B, and O not lying on the same line, which is impossible.

Theorem. *Every two great circles of the same sphere bisect each other.*

The center O (Figure 107) lies in each of the planes of the two great circles, and hence lies in the intersection line of these planes. Therefore this line is a diameter of each of the great circles, and hence bisects the circles.

107. Planes tangent to a ball.

Definition. A plane that has only one common point with a ball is called **tangent** to the ball. Existence of tangent planes is established by the following theorem.

Theorem. *The plane (P, Figure 108) perpendicular to a radius (OA) at the endpoint, lying on the surface of the ball, is tangent to it.*

On the plane P, take any point B and draw the line OB. Since OB is a slant, and OA is the perpendicular to P, we have: $OB > OA$. Therefore the point B lies outside the spherical surface. Thus the plane P has only one common point A with the ball, and hence the plane P is tangent to it.

Converse theorem. *A tangent plane* (P, Figure 108) *is perpendicular to the radius* (OA) *drawn to the point of tangency.*

Since the point A of tangency is the only common point of the plane P and the ball, any other point B of the plane P lies outside the spherical surface, i.e. is farther from the center than the point A. Therefore OA is the shortest segment from the point O to the plane, i.e. OA is perpendicular to P.

A line that has only one common point with a ball is called **tangent** to it. It is easy to see that there are infinitely many lines tangent to the ball at a given point of the spherical surface. Namely, every line (AC, Figure 108) passing through the given point (A) and lying on the plane, tangent to the ball at this point, is tangent to the ball at this point.

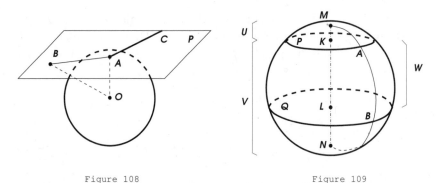

Figure 108   Figure 109

108. Spherical segments and frusta. A plane (P, Figure 109) intersecting a ball divides it into two solids (U and V), either of which is called a **dome** or a **spherical segment**. The disk found in the cross section is called the **base** of the spherical segment. The segment KM of the diameter perpendicular to the base is called the **altitude** of the spherical segment U. The surface of a spherical segment consists of two parts: the base, and a part of the sphere, which will be called the **lateral surface** of the spherical segment.

The part of a ball (W, Figure 109) enclosed between two parallel planes (P and Q) is called a **zone** or **spherical frustum**. The disks found in the cross sections of the ball by these planes are called the **bases** of the spherical frustum. The part of the spherical surface enclosed between the bases is called the **lateral surface** of the spherical frustum, and the part KL of the diameter perpendicular to them, the **altitude**.

Lateral surfaces of spherical segments and frusta can be considered as surfaces of revolution. When the semicircle $MABN$ is rotated about the diameter MN, the arcs MA and AB describe lateral surfaces of the spherical segment U and frustum W. To determine areas of such surfaces, we will first establish the following lemma.

109. Lemma. *The lateral surface area of each of the three solids: a cone, conical frustum, and cylinder, is equal to the product of the altitude of the solid and the circumference of a circle whose radius is the perpendicular to a generatrix from its midpoint up to the axis.*

(1) Let a cone be formed by rotating the right triangle ABC (Figure 110) about the leg AC. If D is the midpoint of the generatrix AB, then the lateral surface area s of the cone is (see Corollary 1 in §97):

$$s = 2\pi \cdot BC \cdot AD. \qquad (*)$$

Drawing $DE \perp AB$ we obtain two similar triangles ABC and EAD (they are right and have a common angle A), from which we derive: $BC : ED = AC : AD$, and therefore $BC \cdot AD = ED \cdot AC$. Substituting into $(*)$, we find:

$$s = 2\pi \cdot ED \cdot AC \quad \text{as required.}$$

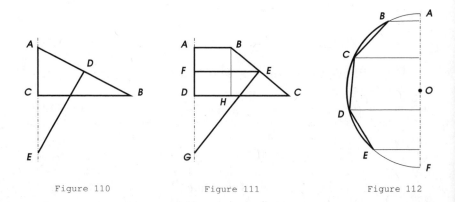

Figure 110   Figure 111   Figure 112

(2) Let a conical frustum be obtained by rotating the trapezoid $ABCD$ (Figure 111) about the side AD. Drawing the midline EF, we find the lateral surface area s of the conical frustum (see Corollary 2 in §99):

$$s = 2\pi \cdot EF \cdot BC. \qquad (**)$$

Draw $EG \perp BC$ and $BH \perp DC$. We obtain two similar right triangles EFG and BHC (sides of one of them are perpendicular to the sides of the other). From them, we derive: $EF : BH = EG : BC$, and therefore $EF \cdot BC = BH \cdot EG = AD \cdot EG$. Substituting this into (**), we conclude:

$$s = 2\pi \cdot EG \cdot AD \quad \text{as required.}$$

(3) The lemma holds true for a cylinder as well, since the circle in the formulation of the lemma is congruent to the circle of the cylinder's base.

110. Areas of spheres and their parts. The **area** of the lateral surface of a spherical frustum, formed by rotating any arc (BE, see Figure 112) of a semicircle about the diameter (AF), is defined to be the limit to which the area of the surface, formed by rotating (about the same diameter) a regular broken line ($BCDE$) inscribed into this arc, tends as the sides of the broken line decrease indefinitely (and therefore their number increases indefinitely).

This definition also applies to the lateral surface area of a spherical segment, and to the entire spherical surface. In the latter case, the broken line is to be inscribed into the entire semicircle.

111. Theorem. *The lateral surface area of a spherical segment (or spherical frustum) is equal to the product of the altitude of the segment (respectively, of the frustum) and the circumference of the great circle.*

Let the lateral surface of a spherical segment be formed by rotating the arc AF (Figure 113). Into this arc, inscribe a regular broken line $ACDEF$ with any number of sides. The surface obtained by rotating this broken line consists of the parts formed by rotating the sides AC, CD, DE, etc. Each of the parts is the lateral surface of a cone (when the rotated side is AC), or conical frustum (when the rotated sides are CD, EF, etc.), or a cylinder (if the rotated side is DE, and $DE \| AB$). Therefore we can apply the previous lemma. For this, notice that each perpendicular erected at the midpoint of the generatrix up to the axis is an apothem a of the broken line. Denote by s_{AC}, s_{CD}, s_{DE}, etc. the lateral surface area obtained respectively by rotating the side AC, CD, DE, etc. Then we have:

$$s_{AC} = AC' \cdot 2\pi a,$$
$$s_{CD} = C'D' \cdot 2\pi a,$$
$$s_{DE} = D'E' \cdot 2\pi a, \quad \text{etc.}$$

Adding these equalities term-wise, we find that the area s_{ACDEF} of the surface formed by rotating the broken line $ACDEF$ is given by:

$$s_{ACDEF} = AF' \cdot 2\pi a.$$

As the number of sides of the regular broken line increases indefinitely, the apothem a tends to a limit congruent to the radius R of the sphere, and the segment AF', which is the altitude h of the spherical segment, remains unchanged. Therefore the limit s, to which the area of the surface obtained by rotating the broken line tends, and which is taken for the definition of the lateral surface area of the spherical segment, is given by the formula:

$$s = h \cdot 2\pi R = 2\pi Rh.$$

Consider now the case when the broken line is inscribed into any arc CF (rather than AF), and thus generates under rotation the lateral surface of a spherical frustum. The above argument remains the same and leads to the same conclusion about the lateral surface area s' of the spherical frustum:

$$s' = h' \cdot 2\pi R = 2\pi Rh',$$

where h' denotes the altitude $C'F'$ of the spherical frustum.

112. Theorem. *The surface area of a sphere is equal to the product of the circumference of the great circle and the diameter,* or equivalently, *the surface area of a sphere is equal to four times the area of the great disk.*

The area of the sphere, obtained by rotating the semicircle ADB (Figure 113), can be considered as the sum of the surface areas formed by rotating the arcs AD and DB. Therefore, applying the previous theorem, we obtain for the area s of the sphere:

$$s = 2\pi R \cdot AD' + 2\pi R \cdot D'B = 2\pi R(AD' + D'B) = 2\pi R \cdot 2R = 4\pi R^2.$$

Corollaries. (1) *The areas of spheres have the same ratio as the squares of their radii, or diameters,* since denoting by s and S the areas of two spheres of radii r and R, we find:

$$s : S = 4\pi r^2 : 4\pi R^2 = r^2 : R^2 = (2r)^2 : (2R)^2.$$

(2) *The area of a sphere is equal to the lateral surface area of the cylinder circumscribed about it* (Figure 114), because the radius of the cylinder's base coincides with the radius R of the sphere, the

altitude with the diameter $2R$, and hence the lateral surface area is $2\pi R \cdot 2R = 4\pi R^2$.

(3) Moreover, *on the circumscribed cylinder* (Figure 114), *the part of the lateral surface, enclosed between any two plane sections perpendicular to the axis, has the same area as the part of the sphere enclosed between these planes.* Indeed, if h denotes the distance between the planes, then the area enclosed by them on the cylinder is equal to $2\pi Rh$, which coincides (according to §111) with the area of the corresponding part on the sphere.

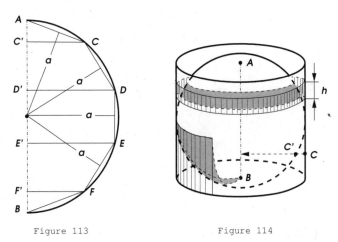

Figure 113   Figure 114

Remark. In fact, the coincidence between corresponding areas on a sphere and on the circumscribed cylinder holds true for spherical regions of arbitrary shape. More precisely, to a point C (Figure 114) on the lateral surface of the circumscribed cylinder, associate the point C' on the spherical surface by dropping the perpendicular from C to the axis AB of the cylinder and taking the point of its intersection with the sphere. Applying this construction to each point of any region on the lateral surface of the cylinder, we obtain the corresponding region on the sphere, and *vice versa*, any region on the sphere corresponds this way to a certain region on the cylindrical surface. Taking into account Corollary 3, as well as the the rotational symmetry of both the cylinder and the sphere about the axis AB, it is not hard to show that *corresponding regions are equivalent.*

This fact is useful in cartography. Namely, one way of exhibiting the surface of the Globe on a geographical map — the so-called *Lambert's equal-area cylindrical projection* — consists in projecting the sphere to the cylindrical surface as explained above (i.e. away from

the axis passing through the poles) and then unrolling the cylinder
into the rectangular net (see §100). While it is generally impossible
to exhibit without distortion the surface of a sphere on a plane map,
this method has the advantage of preserving proportions between
the *areas* of regions. For instance, the Antarctic may appear in this
map to have disproportionately large size (because the South pole is
represented on the cylinder by the whole circle of the bottom base),
but in fact the image of the Antarctic occupies the same fraction of
the map as the continent itself of the Earth's surface.

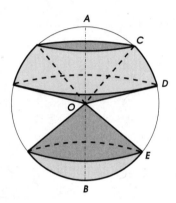

Figure 115

113. Spherical sectors. The solid obtained by rotating a sector
(COD, Figure 115) of a disk about a diameter (AB) not intersecting
the arc of the sector is called a **spherical sector**. This solid is
bounded by the lateral surfaces of two cones and the lateral surface
of a spherical frustum. The latter is called the **base** of the spherical
sector. When the axis of rotation (BO) coincides with one of the
radii of the disk sector (e.g. of BOE), the resulting spherical sector is
bounded by the lateral surfaces of a cone and of a spherical segment.
As an extreme case of a spherical sector, the entire ball is obtained
by rotating a semi-disk about its diameter.

To evaluate the volume of a spherical sector, we need to prove
the following lemma.

114. Lemma. *If a triangle ABC (Figure 117) is rotated about
an axis AM, lying in the plane of the triangle and passing
through the vertex A, but not intersecting the side BC, then
the volume v of the solid of revolution thus obtained is equal
to the product of the surface area s formed by rotating the
side BC and $\frac{1}{3}$ of the altitude h dropped from the vertex A.*

Consider the following three cases.

(1) The axis coincides with the side AB (Figure 116). In this case the volume v is equal to the sum of the volumes of the two cones obtained by rotating the right triangles BCD and DCA. The first volume is $\frac{1}{3}\pi CD^2 \cdot DB$, the second $\frac{1}{3}\pi CD^2 \cdot DA$, and hence

$$v = \frac{1}{3}\pi CD^2(DB + DA) = \frac{1}{3}\pi CD \cdot CD \cdot BA.$$

The product $CD \cdot BA$ is equal to $BC \cdot h$ since each expresses twice the area of $\triangle ABC$. Therefore

$$v = \frac{1}{3}\pi CD \cdot BC \cdot h.$$

But, according to Corollary 1 in §97, the product $\pi CD \cdot BC$ is the lateral surface area of the cone obtained by rotating $\triangle BCD$. Thus $v = sh/3$.

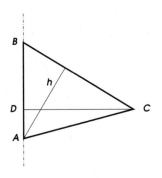

Figure 116

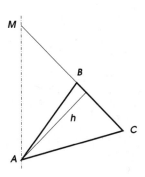

Figure 117

(2) The axis does not coincide with AB and is not parallel to BC (Figure 117). In this case the volume v is the difference of the volumes v_{AMC} and v_{AMB} of the solids obtained by rotating $\triangle AMC$ and $\triangle AMB$. Using the result of the first case, we find:

$$v_{AMC} = \frac{h}{3}s_{MC}, \quad v_{AMB} = \frac{h}{3}s_{MB}$$

where s_{MC} and s_{MB} are surface areas obtained by rotating MC and MB. Therefore

$$v = \frac{h}{3}(s_{MC} - s_{MB}) = \frac{h}{3}s.$$

(3) The axis is parallel to the side BC (Figure 118). Then the volume v is equal to the volume v_{BCDE} of the cylinder, obtained by rotating the rectangle $BCDE$, minus the sum of the volumes v_{AEB} and v_{ADC} of the cones, obtained by rotating $\triangle AEB$ and $\triangle ADC$. Since bases of these solids have the same radius equal h, we find:

$$v_{BCDE} = \pi h^2 \cdot ED, \quad v_{AEB} = \frac{1}{3}\pi h^2 \cdot AE, \quad v_{ADC} = \frac{1}{3}\pi h^2 \cdot AD,$$

and therefore

$$v = \pi h^2 \left(ED - \frac{1}{3}AE - \frac{1}{3}AD \right) = \pi h^2 \left(ED - \frac{1}{3}ED \right) = \frac{2}{3}\pi h^2 \cdot ED.$$

The product $2\pi h \cdot ED$ expresses the area s of the surface obtained by rotating the side BC. Thus $v = sh/3$.

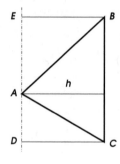
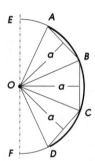

Figure 118   Figure 119

115. Volumes of spherical sectors. Given a spherical sector, obtained by rotating a disk sector $(AOD$ Figure 119) about a diameter (EF), we inscribe into the arc (AD) of the disk sector a regular broken line $(ABCD)$, and form a solid of revolution by rotating about the same diameter the polygon $(OABCD)$, bounded by the broken line and by the extreme radii $(OA$ and $OD)$. The **volume** of the spherical sector is defined to be the limit to which the volume of the solid of revolution tends as the number of sides of the regular broken line increases indefinitely.

116. Theorem. *The volume of a spherical sector is equal to the product of the surface area of its base and a third of the radius.*

Let the spherical sector be obtained by rotating the disk sector AOD (Figure 119) about the diameter EF, and let $ABCD$ be a regular broken line with any number of sides inscribed into the arc AD. Denote by V the volume of the solid obtained by rotating the polygon $OABCD$. This volume is the sum of the volumes obtained by rotating the triangles OAB, OBC, etc. about the axis EF. To each of these volumes, we apply the lemma of §114 and note that the altitudes of the triangles are congruent to the apothem a of the regular broken line. Thus we have:

$$V = s_{AB}\frac{a}{3} + s_{BC}\frac{a}{3} + \cdots = S\frac{a}{3},$$

where we denote by s_{AB}, s_{BC}, etc. and by S the areas of surfaces obtained by rotating sides AB, BC, etc. and the whole broken line $ABCD$ respectively.

Imagine now that the number of sides of the broken line increases indefinitely. Then the apothem a tends to the radius R, and the area S tends to a limit s (see §110), equal to the lateral surface area of the spherical frustum (or spherical segment) formed by rotating the arc AD. The latter surface is the base of the spherical sector. Therefore the volume v of the spherical sector is given by the formula:

$$v = \text{ limit of } V = s\frac{R}{3}.$$

Notice that this argument remains valid if one or even both radii of the disk sector coincide with the axis of revolution.

117. The volume of the ball. Applying the previous result to the extreme case of a semi-disk rotated about its diameter, we obtain the following corollary.

Corollary 1. *The volume of a ball is equal to the product of its surface area and a third of the radius.*

Corollary 2. As we have seen §111, the lateral surface area of a spherical segment or spherical frustum is given by the formula $2\pi Rh$ where R denotes the radius and h the altitude of the segment or frustum. Using this expression for the surface area s of the base of a spherical sector, we find:

$$\text{volume of a spherical sector } = 2\pi Rh \cdot \frac{R}{3} = \frac{2}{3}\pi R^2 h.$$

For the entire ball, when the altitude h is a diameter $D = 2R$, we have:

$$\text{volume of the ball } = \frac{4}{3}\pi R^3 = \frac{4}{3}\pi\left(\frac{D}{2}\right) = \frac{1}{6}\pi D^3.$$

From this, it is evident that *volumes of balls have the same ratio as the cubes of their radii or diameters.*

Corollary 3. *The surface area and the volume of a ball are equal to two thirds of the total surface area and the volume respectively of the cylinder circumscribed about this ball.*

Indeed, the cylinder circumscribed about a ball has the altitude congruent to the diameter of the ball, and the radius of the base congruent to the radius of the ball. Therefore the total surface area t and the volume v of this cylinder are respectively:

$$t = 2\pi R \cdot 2R + 2\pi R^2 = 6\pi R^2, \text{ and } v = \pi R^2 \cdot 2R = 2\pi R^3.$$

Thus $\frac{2}{3}t = 4\pi R^2$ and $\frac{2}{3}v = \frac{4}{3}\pi R^3$, which coincide with the surface area and the volume of the ball respectively.

118. Remarks. (1) Corollary 3 was proved in the 3rd century B.C. by **Archimedes of Syracuse**. Being very fond of this result, Archimedes requested that when he was dead, it would be inscribed on his tomb. This request was honored by the Roman general Marcellus, whose soldier killed Archimedes during the capture of Syracuse in 212 B.C. A famous Roman statesman Cicero, who lived in the 1st century A.D., describes how he managed to locate Archimedes' forgotten grave by looking for a monument featuring a sphere and a cylinder, and was even able to read the verse carved on the tomb.

(2) As a useful exercise, we suggest the reader prove that the surface area and the volume of a ball are equal to $\frac{4}{9}$ of the total surface and the volume respectively of the circumscribed cone, whose generatrix is congruent to the diameter of the base. Combining this proposition with Corollary 3, we can write the following identity, where Q stands for either surface area or volume:

$$\frac{Q_{\text{ball}}}{4} = \frac{Q_{\text{cylinder}}}{6} = \frac{Q_{\text{cone}}}{9}.$$

(3) The formula for the volume of a ball can be easily derived from Cavalieri's principle (§66). Indeed, place a ball of radius R onto a plane P (Figure 120), and place onto the same plane the cylinder whose diameter of the base and altitude are congruent to $2R$ (i.e. the cylinder that can be circumscribed about the ball of radius R). Imagine now that from the cylinder, two cones are removed, each having the midpoint of the cylinder's axis for its vertex, and one of the cylinder's bases for its base. The remaining solid turns out to have the same volume as the ball. To show this, draw any section plane parallel to the plane P, and denote the distance from the center

of the ball to this plane by d, and the radius of the cross section of the ball by r. Then the area of this cross section is equal to $\pi r^2 = \pi(R^2 - d^2)$. The cross section of the solid remaining from the cylinder is a ring whose exterior circle has radius R and interior d (since the angle between the axis of the cone and its generatrices is $45°$). Therefore the area of the ring is equal to $\pi R^2 - \pi d^2 = \pi(R^2 - d^2)$. We see that cross sections of both solids by planes parallel to P have the same areas, and hence the solids, according to Cavalieri's principle, have the same volume. For the solid remaining from the cylinder, this volume is equal to the volume of the cylinder less twice the volume of the cone:

$$\pi R^2 \cdot 2R - 2 \cdot \frac{1}{3}\pi R^2 \cdot R = 2\pi R^3 - \frac{2}{3}\pi R^3 = \frac{4}{3}\pi R^3,$$

which thus expresses the volume of the ball of radius R.

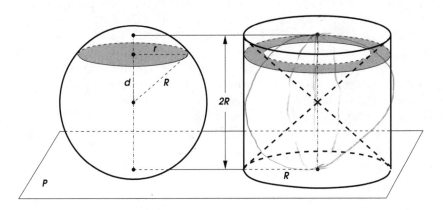

Figure 120

(4) The volume of a ball can also be derived by the following simple (although not quite rigorous) argument. Imagine that the entire surface of the ball is partitioned into very small pieces, and that all points on the contour of each piece are connected by radii to the center of the ball. Thus the ball becomes partitioned into a large number of small solids. Each of them can be considered (approximately) as a pyramid with the vertex at the center. The volume of a pyramid is equal to the product of the area of its base and a third of the altitude (which can be taken to be the radius R of the ball). Therefore the volume v of the ball, equal to the sum of

the volumes of the pyramids, is expressed as:

$$v = s \cdot \frac{1}{3}R,$$

where s denotes the sum of the areas of the bases of all the pyramids. But this sum constitutes the surface area of the ball, i.e.

$$v = 4\pi R^2 \cdot \frac{R}{3} = \frac{4}{3}\pi R^3.$$

Thus the volume of the ball can be expressed through its surface area. Conversely, the area s of the sphere can be found from the volume of the ball:

$$s \cdot \frac{1}{3}R = \frac{4}{3}\pi R^3, \text{ and hence } s = 4\pi R^2.$$

(5) In fact the above argument applies to any part of the ball known as a solid angle. On the surface of the ball, consider a region B bounded by a closed curve C, and connect all points of this curve with the center of the ball by radii. The resulting surface (it is a conical surface in the general sense of §92, with the curve C as the directrix and the radii as generatrices) bounds the part of the ball called a **solid angle** with the base B and the **vertex** at the center. Dividing the base into many small pieces and following the argument in Remark 4, we conclude that the volume V of the part of the solid angle inside the ball of radius R is related to the area S of the base by the formula: $V = SR/3$.

EXERCISES

190. Find the geometric locus of the projections of a given point in space to planes passing through another given point.

191. Find the geometric locus of the centers of the cross sections of a given ball by planes containing a given line. Consider separately the cases when the line intersects the ball, is tangent to it, or does not intersect it.

192. Find the geometric locus of the centers of the cross sections of a given ball by planes passing through a given point. Consider separately the cases when the point lies inside, on the surface, or outside the ball.

193. On the surface of a given ball, find the geometric locus of the tangency points with lines drawn from a given point outside the ball and tangent to the sphere.

194. Prove that all segments drawn from a given point outside a given ball and tangent to it at their endpoint are congruent to each other.

195. The segment connecting the centers of two balls is called their **line of centers**. Prove that if two spheres are **tangent** to each other (i.e. have only one common point) then the tangency point lies on the line of centers (or its extension, if one ball lies inside the other). Derive that tangent spheres have a common tangent plane at their tangency point, and this plane is perpendicular to the line of centers.

196. Prove that two spheres are tangent if and only if their line of centers is congruent to the sum or difference of their radii.

197. Prove that if in a tetrahedron, the three sums of pairs of opposite edges are congruent, then the vertices are the centers of four balls pairwise tangent to each other.

198.⋆ Prove that if vertices of a tetrahedron are centers of pairwise tangent balls, then all the six common tangent planes at the points of tangency of these pairs of balls pass through the same point.

199. Find a necessary and sufficient condition for all edges of a tetrahedron to be tangent to the same ball.

200. A sphere tangent to all faces of a polyhedron or polyhedral angle is called **inscribed** into it. Find the geometric locus of the centers of spheres inscribed into a given trihedral angle.

201. Find the geometric locus of points in space equidistant from three given points.

202. On a given plane, find the geometric locus of points of tangency of balls of a fixed radius r, which are tangent to the plane and to a given ball of radius a tangent to it.

203.⋆ On a given plane, find the geometric locus of the points of tangency of this plane with spheres passing through two given points outside the plane.

204. Prove that any tetrahedron possesses a unique inscribed and unique circumscribed sphere. (A sphere is called **circumscribed** about a polyhedron if all of its vertices lie on the sphere.)

205. In a trihedral angle all of whose plane angles are right, two spheres tangent to each other are inscribed. Compute the ratio of their radii.

206. Prove that about any regular pyramid, a unique ball can be circumscribed, and its center lies on the altitude.

207. Prove that into any regular pyramid, a unique ball can be inscribed, and its center lies on the altitude.

208. Compute the plane angle at the vertex of a regular quadrangular pyramid, if the centers of the inscribed and circumscribed balls coincide.

209. Compute the radius of the ball circumscribed about a cube whose side is 1 *m*.

210.* Prove that if in a polyhedron, all of whose polyhedral angles are trihedral, each face can be circumscribed by a circle, then the polyhedron can be circumscribed by a sphere.

211.* Prove that if into a prism, a ball can be inscribed, then the lateral surface area of the prism is equal to two thirds of the total surface area.

212. Prove that into a conical frustum, a sphere can be inscribed if and only if the sum of the radii of the bases is congruent to the generatrix.

213.* Prove that into a conical frustum, a sphere can be inscribed if and only if the altitude is the geometric mean between the diameters of the bases.

214. The diameter of Mars is twice as small, and of Jupiter is 11 times greater, than the diameter of Earth. By how many times do the surface area and the volume of Jupiter exceed those of Mars?

215. A tall cylindrical vessel with the radius of the base 6 *cm* is half-filled with water. By how much will the water level rise after a ball of radius 3 *cm* is sunk in the vessel?

216. A hollow iron ball of radius 15.5 *cm* is floating in water being half-submersed in it. How thick is the shell, if the specific gravity of iron is 7.75 g/cm^3?

217. Compute the volume and lateral surface area of a conical frustum, whose generatrix is 21 *cm*, and the radii of the bases are 27 *cm* and 18 *cm*.

218. Given a ball of radius 113 *cm*, find the distance from the center to a cross section plane, if the ratio of the lateral surface area of the smaller spherical segment, cut out by the plane, to the lateral surface area of the cone, which has the same base as the spherical segment and the vertex at the center of the ball, is 7 : 4.

219. Along a diameter of a ball of radius 2 *cm*, a cylindrical hole of radius 1 *cm* is drilled. Compute the volume of the remaining part of the ball.

220. Compute the volume of the ball inscribed into a cone whose base has radius $r = 5$ *cm*, and generatrix is $l = 13$ *cm* long.

221. A disk inscribed into an equilateral triangle. Compute the ratio of the volumes of the solids obtained by rotating the disk and triangle about an altitude of the triangle.

222. Prove that the volume of a polyhedron circumscribed about a ball is equal to one third of the product of the radius of the ball and the surface area of the polyhedron.

223. A ball is tangent to all edges of a regular tetrahedron. Which of the solids has greater: (a) volume, (b) surface area?

224. Compute the volume and surface area of the solid which consists of all those points in space whose distance from (at least one point inside or on the surface of) a given cube with the edge a does not exceed r.

225.* A solid consists of all points in space whose distance from (at least one point inside or on the boundary of) a given *polygon* of area s and semiperimeter p does not exceed r. Prove that the volume V and the surface area S of the solid are given by the formulas:

$$V = 2rs + \pi r^2 p + \frac{4}{3}\pi r^3, \quad S = 2s + 2\pi r p + 4\pi r^2.$$

226. Prove that the surface area and volume of a ball are equal to 4/9 of the total surface area and volume respectively of the circumscribed cone whose generatrix is congruent to the diameter of the base.

227.* Prove that the volume of a spherical segment is equal to the volume of the cylinder, whose base has the radius congruent to the altitude of the segment, and whose altitude is congruent to the radius of the ball less a third of the altitude of the segment, i.e.

$$v = \pi h^2 (R - \frac{h}{3}),$$

where v denotes the volume of the segment, h its altitude, and R the radius of the ball.

228.* Prove that the volume of a spherical frustum is given by the formula:

$$v = \pi \frac{h^3}{6} + \pi(r_1^2 + r_2^2)\frac{h}{2},$$

where h is the altitude of the frustum, and r_1 and r_2 are the radii of the bases.

229. Given a polyhedral angle, intersect it with a sphere of radius R centered at the vertex, and show that the area S of the part of the sphere inside the angle is proportional to R^2.

Remark. The ratio $S : R^2$ can be considered as some **measure** of the polyhedral angle (or, more generally, any solid angle).

230. Compute the measure of the polyhedral angles of the cube.

231. Compute the measure of the solid angle at the vertex of a cone with the generatrix l and altitude h.

Chapter 4

VECTORS AND FOUNDATIONS

1 Algebraic operations with vectors

119. Definition of vectors. In physics, some quantities (e.g. distances, volumes, temperatures, or masses) are completely characterized by their magnitudes, expressed with respect to a chosen unit by real numbers. These quantities are called *scalars*. Some others (e.g. velocities, accelerations, or forces) cannot be characterized only by their magnitudes, because they may differ also by their directions. Such quantities are called *vectors*.

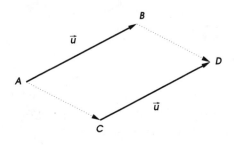

Figure 121

To represent a vector quantity geometrically, we draw an arrow connecting two points in space, e.g. A with B (Figure 121). We call it a **directed segment** with the **tail** A and **head** B, and indicate this in writing as $\overrightarrow{AB}$.

The same **vector** can be represented by different directed segments. By definition, two directed segments ($\overrightarrow{AB}$ and $\overrightarrow{CD}$) **represent the same vector** if they are obtained from each other by translation (§72). In other words, the directed segments must have the same length, lie on the same line or two parallel lines, and point toward the same direction (out of two possible ones). When this is the case, we write $\overrightarrow{AB} = \overrightarrow{CD}$ and say that the vectors represented by these directed segments are **equal**. Note that $\overrightarrow{AB} = \overrightarrow{CD}$ exactly when the quadrilateral $ABDC$ is a parallelogram.

We will also denote a vector by a single lower case letter with an arrow over it, e.g. the vector $\vec{u}$ (Figure 121).

120. Addition of vectors. Given two vectors $\vec{u}$ and $\vec{v}$, their **sum** $\vec{u} + \vec{v}$ is defined as follows. Pick any directed segment $\overrightarrow{AB}$ (Figure 122) representing the vector $\vec{u}$. Represent the vector $\vec{v}$ by the directed segment $\overrightarrow{BC}$ whose tail B coincides with the head of $\overrightarrow{AB}$. Then the directed segment $\overrightarrow{AC}$ represents the sum $\vec{u} + \vec{v}$.

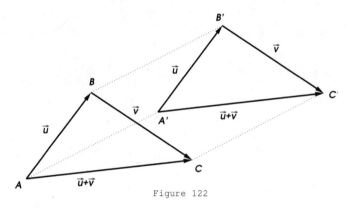

Figure 122

The sum of vectors thus defined does not depend on the choice of the directed segment representing the vector $\vec{u}$. Indeed, if another directed segment $\overrightarrow{A'B'}$ is chosen to represent $\vec{u}$, and respectively the directed segment $\overrightarrow{B'C'}$ (with the tail B') represents $\vec{v}$, then the quadrilaterals $ABB'A'$ and $BCC'B'$ are parallelograms. Therefore the segments AA' and CC' are congruent, parallel, and have the same direction (since they are congruent to, parallel to, and have the same direction as BB'), and hence the quadrilateral $ACC'A'$ is a parallelogram too. Thus the directed segments $\overrightarrow{AC}$ and $\overrightarrow{A'C'}$ represent the same vector.

Addition of vectors is **commutative**, i.e. the sum does not depend on the order of the summands:

$$\vec{u} + \vec{v} = \vec{v} + \vec{u} \text{ for all vectors } \vec{u} \text{ and } \vec{v}.$$

Indeed, represent the vectors by directed segments $\overrightarrow{AB}$ and $\overrightarrow{AD}$ with the same tail A (Figure 123). In the plane of the triangle ABD, draw lines $BC\|AD$ and $DC\|AB$, and denote by C their intersection point. Then $ABCD$ is a parallelogram, and hence $\overrightarrow{DC} = \vec{u}$, $\overrightarrow{BC} = \vec{v}$. Therefore the diagonal $\overrightarrow{AC}$ of the parallelogram is a directed segment representing both $\vec{u} + \vec{v}$ and $\vec{v} + \vec{u}$.

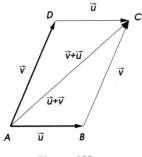
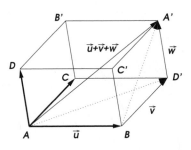

Figure 123   Figure 124

Addition of vectors is **associative**, i.e. the sum of three (or more) vectors does not depend on the order in which the additions are performed:

$$(\vec{u} + \vec{v}) + \vec{w} = \vec{u} + (\vec{v} + \vec{w}) \text{ for all vectors } \vec{u}, \vec{v}, \text{ and } \vec{w}.$$

Indeed, represent the vectors $\vec{u}$, $\vec{v}$, and $\vec{w}$ by directed segments $\overrightarrow{AB}$, $\overrightarrow{AC}$, and $\overrightarrow{AD}$ with the same tail A (Figure 124), and then construct the parallelepiped $ABCDA'B'C'D'$ all of whose edges are parallel to AB, AC, or AD. Then the diagonal directed segment $\overrightarrow{AA'}$ represents the sum $\vec{u} + \vec{v} + \vec{w}$ regardless of the ordering of the summands or the order in which the additions are performed. For instance,

$$\overrightarrow{AA'} = \overrightarrow{AB} + \overrightarrow{BA'} = \overrightarrow{AB} + (\overrightarrow{BD'} + \overrightarrow{D'A'}) = \vec{u} + (\vec{v} + \vec{w}),$$

since $\overrightarrow{BD'} = \overrightarrow{AC} = \vec{v}$ and $\overrightarrow{D'A'} = \overrightarrow{AD} = \vec{w}$. At the same time,

$$\overrightarrow{AA'} = \overrightarrow{AD'} + \overrightarrow{D'A'} = (\overrightarrow{AB} + \overrightarrow{BD'}) + \overrightarrow{D'A'} = (\vec{u} + \vec{v}) + \vec{w}.$$

121. Multiplication of vectors by scalars. Given a scalar
(i.e. a real number) α and a vector $\vec{u}$, one can form a new vector
denoted $\alpha\vec{u}$ and called the **product** of the scalar and the vector.

Namely, represent the vector $\vec{u}$ by any directed segment $\overrightarrow{AB}$ (Figure 125) and apply to it the homothety (see §§70–72) with the coefficient $\alpha \neq 0$ with respect to any center S. Then the resulting
directed segment $\overrightarrow{A'B'}$ represents the vector $\alpha\vec{u}$. In other words,
since the triangles SAB and $SA'B'$ are similar, the directed segment
$\overrightarrow{A'B'}$ representing the vector $\alpha\vec{u}$ is parallel to $\overrightarrow{AB}$ (or lies on the same
line), is $|\alpha|$ times longer than $\overrightarrow{AB}$, and has the same direction as $\overrightarrow{AB}$
when α is positive, and the opposite direction when α is negative.

We will often call vectors $\vec{u}$ and $\alpha\vec{u}$ **proportional** and refer to
the number α as the coefficient of proportionality.

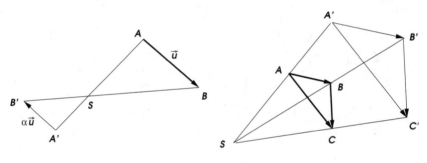

Figure 125   Figure 126

In the special case of $\alpha = 0$, the product $0\vec{u}$ is represented by
any directed segment $\overrightarrow{SS}$ whose tail and head coincide. The corresponding vector is called the **zero vector** and is denoted by $\vec{0}$.
Thus

$$0\vec{u} = \vec{0} \quad \text{for every vector } \vec{u}.$$

Multiplication by scalars is **distributive** *with respect to addition
of vectors,* i.e. for all vectors $\vec{u}$ and $\vec{v}$ and every scalar α we have:

$$\alpha(\vec{u} + \vec{v}) = \alpha\vec{u} + \alpha\vec{v}.$$

Indeed, let the sides of the triangle ABC (Figure 126) represent
respectively: $\overrightarrow{AB}$ the vector $\vec{u}$, $\overrightarrow{BC}$ the vector $\vec{v}$, and $\overrightarrow{AC}$ their sum
$\vec{u} + \vec{v}$, and let $\triangle A'B'C'$ be homothetic to $\triangle ABC$ (with respect to
any center S) with the homothety coefficient α. Then

$$\overrightarrow{A'B'} = \alpha\vec{u}, \quad \overrightarrow{B'C'} = \alpha\vec{v}, \quad \text{and} \quad \overrightarrow{A'C'} = \alpha(\vec{u} + \vec{v}).$$

Since $\overrightarrow{A'C'} = \overrightarrow{A'B'} + \overrightarrow{B'C'}$, the distributivity law follows.

Two more properties[1] of multiplication of vectors by scalars:

$$(\alpha + \beta)\vec{u} = \alpha\vec{u} + \beta\vec{u}, \quad \text{and} \quad (\alpha\beta)\vec{u} = \alpha(\beta\vec{u})$$

follow from the geometric meaning of operations with numbers. Indeed, let $\overrightarrow{OU} = \vec{u}$ (Figure 127). The infinite line OU can be identified with the number line (see Book I, §153) by taking the segment OU for the unit of length and letting the points O and U represent the numbers 0 and 1 respectively. Then any scalar α is represented on this number line by a unique point A such that $\overrightarrow{OA} = \alpha\overrightarrow{OU}$. Furthermore, addition of vectors on the line and their multiplication by scalars is expressed as addition and multiplication of the corresponding numbers. For example, if B is another point on the line such that $\overrightarrow{OB} = \beta\overrightarrow{OU}$, then the vector sum $\overrightarrow{OA} + \overrightarrow{OB}$ corresponds to the number $\alpha + \beta$ on the number line, i.e. $\alpha\overrightarrow{OU} + \beta\overrightarrow{OU} = (\alpha + \beta)\overrightarrow{OU}$. Similarly, multiplying by a scalar α the vector $\overrightarrow{OB}$ (corresponding to β on the number line) we obtain a new vector corresponding to the product $\alpha\beta$ of the numbers, i.e. $\alpha(\beta\overrightarrow{OU}) = (\alpha\beta)\overrightarrow{OU}$.

Examples. (1) If a vector $\vec{u}$ is represented by a directed segment $\overrightarrow{AB}$, then the opposite directed segment $\overrightarrow{BA}$ represents the vector $(-1)\vec{u}$, also denoted simply by $-\vec{u}$. Note that **opposite vectors** add up to $\vec{0}$. This is obvious from $\overrightarrow{AB} + \overrightarrow{BA} = \overrightarrow{AA} = \vec{0}$, but also follows formally from the distributivity law:

$$\vec{0} = 0\vec{u} = (-1+1)\vec{u} = (-1)\vec{u} + 1\vec{u} = -\vec{u} + \vec{u}.$$

(2) If vectors $\vec{u}$ and $\vec{v}$ are represented by the directed segments $\overrightarrow{AB}$ and $\overrightarrow{AC}$ with a common tail, then the directed segment $\overrightarrow{BC}$ connecting the heads represents the **difference** $\vec{v} - \vec{u}$ (because $\overrightarrow{AB} + \overrightarrow{BC} = \overrightarrow{AC}$).

In applications of vector algebra to geometry, it is often convenient to represent all vectors by directed segments with a common tail, called the **origin**, which can be chosen arbitrarily. Once an origin O is chosen, each point A in space becomes represented by a unique vector, $\overrightarrow{OA}$, called the **radius-vector** of the point A with respect to the origin O.

---

[1]They are called: **distributivity** with respect to addition of scalars, and **associativity** with respect to multiplication by scalars.

122. Problem. *Compute the radius-vector $\vec{m}$ of the barycenter of a triangle ABC* (Figure 128), *given the radius-vectors $\vec{a}$, $\vec{b}$, and $\vec{c}$ of its vertices.*

Recall that the barycenter is the intersection point of the medians. Denote A' the midpoint of the side BC, and on the median AA' mark the point M which divides the median in the proportion $AM : MA' = 2 : 1$. We have: $\overrightarrow{AB} = \vec{b} - \vec{a}$, $\overrightarrow{BC} = \vec{c} - \vec{b}$, and hence

$$\overrightarrow{AA'} = \overrightarrow{AB} + \frac{1}{2}\overrightarrow{BC} = \vec{b} - \vec{a} + \frac{1}{2}\vec{c} - \frac{1}{2}\vec{b} = \frac{1}{2}(\vec{b} + \vec{c} - 2\vec{a}).$$

Therefore

$$\overrightarrow{OM} = \overrightarrow{OA} + \overrightarrow{AM} = \overrightarrow{OA} + \frac{2}{3}\overrightarrow{AA'} = \vec{a} + \frac{1}{3}(\vec{b} + \vec{c} - 2\vec{a}) = \frac{1}{3}(\vec{a} + \vec{b} + \vec{c}).$$

Clearly, the same result remains true for each of the other two medians. Thus the head of the radius-vector

$$\vec{m} = \frac{1}{3}(\vec{a} + \vec{b} + \vec{c})$$

lies on all the three medians and thus coincides with the barycenter. As a by-product, we have obtained a new proof of the concurrency theorem (Book I, §142): *the three medians of a triangle meet at the point dividing each of them in the proportion 2 : 1 counting from the vertex.*

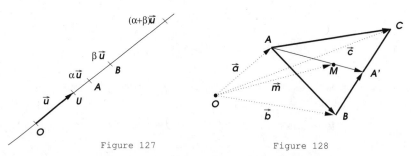

Figure 127   Figure 128

123. The dot product. Given two vectors $\vec{u}$ and $\vec{v}$, their **dot product** $\vec{u} \cdot \vec{v}$ (also known as **scalar product**) is a *number* defined as the product of the lengths of the vectors and the cosine of the angle between their directions. Thus, if the vectors are represented by the directed segments $\overrightarrow{OU}$ and $\overrightarrow{OV}$ (Figure 129), then

$$\vec{u} \cdot \vec{v} = OU \cdot OV \cdot \cos \angle VOU.$$

In particular, the dot product of a vector with itself is equal to the square of the vector's length:

$$\vec{u} \cdot \vec{u} = |\vec{u}|^2, \quad \text{or} \quad |\vec{u}| = \sqrt{\vec{u} \cdot \vec{u}}.$$

If $\theta(\vec{u}, \vec{v})$ denotes the angle between the directions of two non-zero vectors, then

$$\cos \theta(\vec{u}, \vec{v}) = \frac{\vec{u} \cdot \vec{v}}{|\vec{u}||\vec{v}|}.$$

Thus, the dot product operation captures information about distances and angles.

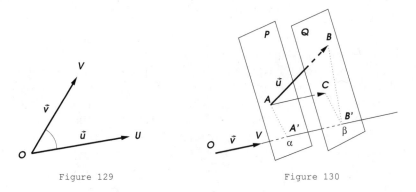

Figure 129   Figure 130

Now let us define the **signed projection** of any vector $\vec{u}$ to the direction of a **unit vector** $\vec{v}$, i.e. assuming that $|\vec{v}| = 1$. Let directed segments $\overrightarrow{AB}$ and $\overrightarrow{OV}$ (Figure 130) represent the two vectors. Consider projections of the points A and B to the line OV. For this, draw through A and B the planes P and Q perpendicular to the line OV until they intersect it at the points A' and B'. Identifying the line OV with the number line, we represent the positions of these points by numbers α and β, and introduce the signed projection as their difference $\beta - \alpha$. It does not depend on the choice of directed segments representing the vectors because it is equal to their dot product: $\beta - \alpha = \vec{u} \cos \theta(\vec{u}, \vec{v})$. Indeed, draw through the point A the line $AC \| OU$, and extend it to the intersection point C with the plane Q. Then $AC = A'B'$ (as segments of parallel lines between two parallel planes), and $\angle BAC = \theta(\vec{u}, \vec{v})$. The sign of $\beta - \alpha$ is positive if the direction of $\overrightarrow{A'B'}$ agrees with the direction of $\overrightarrow{OV}$, i.e. whenever $\angle BAC$ is acute, and negative otherwise, i.e. when the angle is obtuse. We find therefore that $\beta - \alpha = AB \cdot \cos \angle BAC = \vec{u} \cdot \vec{v}$.

We obtain the following geometric interpretation of the dot product operation: *the dot product of any vector with a unit vector is equal to the signed projection of the former to the direction of the latter.*

124. Algebraic properties of the dot product.

(1) *The dot product operation is* **symmetric:**

$$\vec{u} \cdot \vec{v} = \vec{v} \cdot \vec{u} \quad \text{for all vectors } \vec{u} \text{ and } \vec{v},$$

because obviously $\cos\theta(\vec{u}, \vec{v}) = \cos\theta(\vec{v}, \vec{u})$.

(2) *The dot product $\vec{u} \cdot \vec{v}$ is* **homogeneous** *(of degree 1) with respect to either vector, i.e. for all vectors $\vec{u}$, $\vec{v}$, and any scalar α*

$$(\alpha\vec{u}) \cdot \vec{v} = \alpha(\vec{u} \cdot \vec{v}) = \vec{u} \cdot (\alpha\vec{v}).$$

It suffices to verify the first equality only (as the second one follows from it due to the symmetricity of the dot product). The length of $\alpha\vec{u}$ is $|\alpha|$ times greater than the length of $\vec{u}$. Therefore the property is obvious for positive (or zero) α since in this case the directions of these vectors coincide. In the case of negative α, the vectors $\vec{u}$ and $\alpha\vec{u}$ have opposite directions (Figure 131). Then the angles they make with the vector $\vec{v}$ are supplementary, so that their cosines are opposite, and the equality remains true.

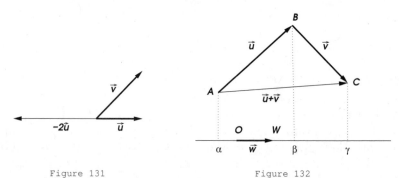

Figure 131   Figure 132

(3) *The dot product is* **additive** *with respect to each of the vectors:*

$$(\vec{u} + \vec{v}) \cdot \vec{w} = \vec{u} \cdot \vec{w} + \vec{v} \cdot \vec{w} \quad \text{and} \quad \vec{w} \cdot (\vec{u} + \vec{v}) = \vec{w} \cdot \vec{u} + \vec{w} \cdot \vec{v}$$

for all vectors $\vec{u}$, $\vec{v}$, and $\vec{w}$. Due to symmetricity, it suffices to verify only the first equality. We may assume that $\vec{w} \neq \vec{0}$ (because otherwise all three terms vanish). Due to homogeneity, dividing each term by the length of the vector $\vec{w}$, one reduces the equality to its special case when $|\vec{w}| = 1$. Let ABC (Figure 132) be a triangle such that $\overrightarrow{AB} = \vec{u}$, $\overrightarrow{BC} = \vec{v}$, and hence $\overrightarrow{AC} = \vec{u} + \vec{v}$. Denote by A', B', and C' the projections of the points A, B, and C to the line of the unit directed segment $\overrightarrow{OW} = \vec{w}$. Considering this line as the number line, represent the projection points by numbers α, β, and γ. Then

$$\vec{u} \cdot \vec{w} = \beta - \alpha, \quad \vec{v} \cdot \vec{w} = \gamma - \beta, \quad \text{and} \quad (\vec{u} + \vec{v}) \cdot \vec{w} = \gamma - \alpha.$$

Since $(\beta - \alpha) + (\gamma - \beta) = \gamma - \alpha$, the required equality holds.

125. Examples. Some applications of the dot product operation are based on the simplicity of its algebraic properties.

(1) *Perpendicular vectors have zero dot product* because $\cos 90° = 0$. Therefore, if we denote by $\vec{u}$ and $\vec{v}$ the legs $\overrightarrow{AB}$ and $\overrightarrow{BC}$ of a right triangle ABC, then its hypotenuse $\overrightarrow{AC}$ is $\vec{u} + \vec{v}$, and the square of its length is computed as follows:

$$(\vec{u} + \vec{v}) \cdot (\vec{u} + \vec{v}) = \vec{u} \cdot (\vec{u} + \vec{v}) + \vec{v} \cdot (\vec{u} + \vec{v}) = \vec{u} \cdot \vec{u} + \vec{v} \cdot \vec{v},$$

since $\vec{u} \cdot \vec{v} = \vec{v} \cdot \vec{u} = 0$. Thus $AC^2 = AB^2 + BC^2$, and so we have re-proved the Pythagorean theorem once again.

(2) More generally, given any triangle ABC, put $\vec{u} = \overrightarrow{AB}$, $\vec{v} = \overrightarrow{AC}$ and compute:

$$BC^2 = (\vec{v} - \vec{u}) \cdot (\vec{v} - \vec{u}) = \vec{v} \cdot \vec{v} - \vec{v} \cdot \vec{u} - \vec{u} \cdot \vec{v} + \vec{u} \cdot \vec{u}$$
$$= \vec{u} \cdot \vec{u} + \vec{v} \cdot \vec{v} - 2\vec{u} \cdot \vec{v} = AB^2 + AC^2 - 2AB \cdot AC \cdot \cos \angle BAC.$$

This is the law of cosines (Book I, §205).

EXERCISES

232. Prove that for every closed broken line $ABCDE$,

$$\overrightarrow{AB} + \overrightarrow{BC} + \cdots + \overrightarrow{DE} + \overrightarrow{EA} = \vec{0}.$$

233. Prove that if the sum of three unit vectors is equal to $\vec{0}$, then the angle between each pair of these vectors is equal to $120°$.

234. Prove that if four unit vectors lying in the same plane add up to $\vec{0}$ then they form two pairs of opposite vectors. Does this remain true if the vectors do not have to lie in the same plane?

235.* Let $ABCDE$ be a regular polygon with the center O. Prove that

$$\overrightarrow{OA} + \overrightarrow{OB} + \cdots + \overrightarrow{OE} = \vec{0}.$$

236. Along three circles lying in the same plane, vertices of a triangle are moving clockwise with the equal constant angular velocities. Find out how the barycenter of the triangle is moving.

237. Prove that if AA' is a median in a triangle ABC, then

$$\overrightarrow{AA'} = \frac{1}{2}(\overrightarrow{AB} + \overrightarrow{AC}).$$

238. Prove that from segments congruent to the medians of a given triangle, another triangle can be formed.

239. Sides of one triangle are parallel to the medians of another. Prove that the medians of the latter triangle are parallel to the sides of the former one.

240. From medians of a given triangle, a new triangle is formed, and from its medians, yet another triangle is formed. Prove that the third triangle is similar to the first one, and find the coefficient of similarity.

241. Midpoints of AB and CD, and of BC and DE are connected by two segments, whose midpoints are also connected. Prove that the resulting segment is parallel to AE and congruent to $\frac{1}{4}AE$.

242. Prove that a point X lies on the line AB if and only if for some scalar α and any origin O the radius-vectors satisfy the equation:

$$\overrightarrow{OX} = \alpha\overrightarrow{OA} + (1 - \alpha)\overrightarrow{OB}.$$

243. Prove that if the vectors $\vec{u} + \vec{v}$ and $\vec{u} - \vec{v}$ are perpendicular, then $|\vec{u}| = |\vec{v}|$.

244. For arbitrary vectors $\vec{u}$ and $\vec{v}$, verify the equality:

$$|\vec{u} + \vec{v}|^2 + |\vec{u} - \vec{v}|^2 = 2|\vec{u}|^2 + 2|\vec{v}|^2,$$

and derive the theorem: the sum of the squares of the diagonals of a parallelogram is equal to the sum of the squares of the sides.

245. Prove that for every triangle ABC and every point X in space,
$$\overrightarrow{XA} \cdot \overrightarrow{BC} + \overrightarrow{XB} \cdot \overrightarrow{CA} + \overrightarrow{XC} \cdot \overrightarrow{AB} = 0.$$

246.* For four arbitrary points A, B, C, and D in space, prove that if the lines AC and BD are perpendicular, then $AB^2 + CD^2 = BC^2 + DA^2$, and *vice versa*.

247. Given a quadrilateral with perpendicular diagonals, show that every quadrilateral, whose sides are respectively congruent to the sides of the given one, has perpendicular diagonals.

248. A regular triangle ABC is inscribed into a circle of radius R. Prove that for every point X of this circle, $XA^2 + XB^2 + XC^2 = 6R^2$.

249.⋆ Let $A_1B_1A_2B_2\ldots A_nB_n$ be a $2n$-gon inscribed into a circle. Prove that the length of the vector $\overrightarrow{A_1B_1} + \overrightarrow{A_2B_2} + \cdots + \overrightarrow{A_nB_n}$ does not exceed the diameter.

Hint: Consider projections of the vertices to any line.

250.⋆ A polyhedron is filled with air under pressure. The pressure force to each face is the vector perpendicular to the face, proportional to the area of the face, and directed to the exterior of the polyhedron. Prove that the sum of these vectors equals $\vec{0}$.

Hint: Take the dot-product with an arbitrary unit vector, and use Corollary 2 of §65.

2 Applications of vectors to geometry

126. Theorem. *If the circumcenter* $(O,$ *Figure 133) of a triangle* (ABC) *is chosen for the origin, then the radius-vector of the orthocenter is equal to the sum of the radius-vectors of the vertices.*

Denote the radius-vectors of the vertices A, B, and C by $\vec{a}$, $\vec{b}$, and $\vec{c}$ respectively. Then $|\vec{a}| = |\vec{b}| = |\vec{c}|$, since O is the circumcenter. Let H be the point in the plane of the triangle such that $\overrightarrow{OH} = \vec{a}+\vec{b}+\vec{c}$. It is required to show that H is the orthocenter. Compute the dot product $\overrightarrow{CH} \cdot \overrightarrow{AB}$. Since $\overrightarrow{CH} = \overrightarrow{OH} - \overrightarrow{OC} = (\vec{a}+\vec{b}+\vec{c}) - \vec{c} = \vec{a}+\vec{b}$, and $\overrightarrow{AB} = \overrightarrow{OB} - \overrightarrow{OA} = \vec{b} - \vec{a}$, we find:

$$\overrightarrow{CH} \cdot \overrightarrow{AB} = (\vec{a} + \vec{b}) \cdot (\vec{b} - \vec{a}) = \vec{b}\cdot\vec{b} - \vec{a}\cdot\vec{a} = |\vec{b}|^2 - |\vec{a}|^2 = 0.$$

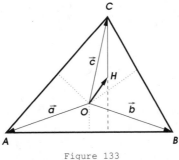

Figure 133

Vanishing of the dot product of two vectors means that these vectors are perpendicular (unless one of them is zero, in which case the angle is, strictly speaking, ill-defined). We conclude that the line CH is perpendicular to AB (unless H and C coincide), i.e. (in either case) the point H lies on the altitude dropped from the vertex C to the side AB, or on the extension of this altitude. Since the same applies to each of the other two altitudes, it follows that the three altitudes, or their extensions, pass through the point H.

Corollaries. (1) We have obtained a new proof of the theorem (Book I, §141): *Altitudes of a triangle are concurrent.*

(2) *In every triangle, the circumcenter O, barycenter M, and orthocenter H are collinear. More precisely, M divides the segment OH in the proportion $OM : MH = 1 : 2$.* Indeed, according to §122, we have:

$$\overrightarrow{OM} = \frac{1}{3}(\vec{a} + \vec{b} + \vec{c}) = \frac{1}{3}\overrightarrow{OH}.$$

Remarks. (1) The segment containing the circumcenter, barycenter, and orthocenter is called **Euler's line** of the triangle (see also Book I, Exercises 226–228).

(2) In the previous theorem, operations with vectors allow one to formulate new results (and re-prove old ones) about familiar notions of plane geometry. In the next example, vectors turn out to be useful although the formulation of the problem does not involve any vectors at all. In such situations, in order to apply vector algebra, points of interest can be represented by their radius-vectors. If it is unclear from the context which of the given points should play the role of the origin, it is advisable (although not necessary) to avoid making any artificial choice. Instead, one can chose an arbitrary point not mentioned in the problem — the resulting conclusion will not depend on this choice.

127. Problem. *Given a triangle ABC (Figure 134), a new triangle $A'B'C'$ is drawn in such a way that A' is centrally symmetric to A with respect to the center B, B' is centrally symmetric to B with respect to the center C, C' is centrally symmetric to C with respect to the center A, and then the triangle ABC is erased. Reconstruct $\triangle ABC$ from $\triangle A'B'C'$ by straightedge and compass.*

Pick an arbitrary point O as the origin, and denote by $\vec{a}$, $\vec{a'}$, $\vec{b}$, etc. the radius-vectors of the points A, A', B, etc. If two points are centrally symmetric with respect to a center, then the radius-vector of the center is equal to the average of the radius-vectors of the points. Therefore, from the hypotheses of the problem, we have:

$$\vec{b} = \frac{1}{2}(\vec{a} + \vec{a'}), \quad \vec{c} = \frac{1}{2}(\vec{b} + \vec{b'}), \quad \vec{a} = \frac{1}{2}(\vec{c} + \vec{c'}).$$

Assuming that $\vec{a'}$, $\vec{b'}$, and $\vec{c'}$ are given, solve this system of equations for $\vec{a}$, $\vec{b}$, and $\vec{c}$. For this, replace $\vec{b}$ in the 2nd equation by its expression from the 1st, and substitute the resulting expression for $\vec{c}$ into the 3rd equation. We obtain:

$$\vec{a} = \frac{1}{2}\left(\vec{c'} + \frac{1}{2}\left(\vec{b'} + \frac{1}{2}\left(\vec{a'} + \vec{a}\right)\right)\right) = \frac{1}{2}\vec{c'} + \frac{1}{4}\vec{b'} + \frac{1}{8}\vec{a'} + \frac{1}{8}\vec{a}.$$

Therefore,

$$\frac{7}{8}\vec{a} = \frac{1}{2}\vec{c'} + \frac{1}{4}\vec{b'} + \frac{1}{8}\vec{a'}, \quad \text{or} \quad \vec{a} = \frac{1}{7}\vec{a'} + \frac{2}{7}\vec{b'} + \frac{4}{7}\vec{c'}.$$

The directed segment $\overrightarrow{OA}$ representing the last vector expression is not hard to construct by straightedge and compass, starting from given directed segments $\vec{a'} = \overrightarrow{OA'}$, $\vec{b'} = \overrightarrow{OB'}$, and $\vec{c'} = \overrightarrow{OC'}$. The vertices B and C of $\triangle ABC$ can be constructed using the expressions:

$$\vec{b} = \frac{1}{7}\vec{b'} + \frac{2}{7}\vec{c'} + \frac{4}{7}\vec{a'} \quad \text{and} \quad \vec{c} = \frac{1}{7}\vec{c'} + \frac{2}{7}\vec{a'} + \frac{4}{7}\vec{b'}.$$

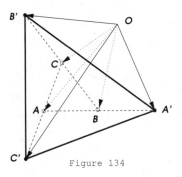

Figure 134

128. The center of mass. By a **material point** we will mean a point in space equipped with a **mass**, which can be any real number. Unless the opposite is specified, we will assume all masses *positive*.[2] The following notion is borrowed from physics.

Given a system of n material points $A_1, A_2, \ldots, A_n$ of masses $m_1, m_2, \ldots, m_n$, their **center of mass** (or **barycenter**) is the material point whose mass m is equal to the total mass of the system:

$$m = m_1 + m_2 + \cdots + m_n,$$

---

[2]When both positive and negative masses occur, we refer to the latter ones as **pseudo-masses**.

and the position A is determined by the condition:

$$m_1 \overrightarrow{AA_1} + m_2 \overrightarrow{AA_2} + \cdots + m_n \overrightarrow{AA_n} = \vec{0}.$$

In other words, the above **weighted sum** of the radius-vectors of the material points with respect to the center of mass as the origin is equal to zero.

With respect to an arbitrary origin O, the radius-vector $\vec{a} = \overrightarrow{OA}$ of the center of mass can be computed in terms of the radius-vectors $\vec{a_1}, \vec{a_2}, \ldots, \vec{a_n}$ of the points. We have:

$$\vec{0} = m_1(\vec{a_1} - \vec{a}) + \cdots + m_n(\vec{a_n} - \vec{a}) = m_1 \vec{a_1} + \cdots + m_n \vec{a_n} - m\vec{a},$$

and therefore

$$\vec{a} = \frac{1}{m}(m_1 \vec{a_1} + m_2 \vec{a_2} + \cdots + m_n \vec{a_n}).$$

This formula establishes the existence and the uniqueness of the mass center of any system of n material points (even with negative masses, as long as the total mass m of the system is non-zero).

Examples. (1) In a system of two material points, we have: $m_1 \overrightarrow{AA_1} + m_2 \overrightarrow{AA_2} = \vec{0}$, or equivalently, $\overrightarrow{AA_1} = -\frac{m_2}{m_1} \overrightarrow{AA_2}$. Hence the center of mass A lies on the segment $A_1 A_2$ (Figure 135), connecting the points, and divides it in the proportion $A_1 A : AA_2 = m_2 : m_1$ (i.e. the mass center is closer to the point of greater mass).

(2) Let $\vec{a}$, $\vec{b}$, and $\vec{c}$ be radius-vectors of three given material points of *equal* mass. Then $\frac{1}{3}(\vec{a} + \vec{b} + \vec{c})$ is the radius-vector of the center of mass. Comparing with §122, we conclude that the center of mass coincides with the barycenter of the triangle with vertices at the three given points.

129. Regrouping. Most applications of centers of mass to geometry rely on their **associativity**, or **regrouping** property.

Theorem. *If a system of material points is divided into two (or more) parts, and then each part is replaced by a single material point representing its center of mass, then the center of mass of the resulting system of two (or more) material points coincides with the center of mass of the original system.*

Say, let A_1, A_2 and A_3, A_4, A_5 (Figure 136) be two parts of a system of five material points with masses $m_1, \ldots, m_5$. We are required to show that if A' and A'' are the positions of the centers of mass of these parts, and $m' = m_1 + m_2$ and $m'' = m_3 + m_4 + m_5$ are their respective masses, then the center of mass of this pair of material points coincides (as a material point, i.e. in regard to both its mass and position) with the center of mass of the whole system of five material points.

Firstly, we note that the sum $m' + m''$ indeed coincides with the total mass $m = m_1 + m_2 + \cdots + m_5$ of the whole system. Secondly, using the radius-vectors $\vec{a'}, \vec{a''}, \vec{a_1}, \ldots, \vec{a_5}$ of the points $A', A'', A_1, \ldots, A_5$ with respect to any origin, we find:

$$\vec{a'} = \frac{1}{m'}(m_1\vec{a_1} + m_2\vec{a_2}), \quad \vec{a''} = \frac{1}{m''}(m_3\vec{a_3} + m_4\vec{a_4} + m_5\vec{a_5}).$$

The center of mass of this pair of material points has the radius-vector

$$\frac{1}{m' + m''}(m'\vec{a'} + m''\vec{a''}) = \frac{1}{m}(m_1\vec{a_1} + m_2\vec{a_2} + m_3\vec{a_3} + m_4\vec{a_4} + m_5\vec{a_5}).$$

Thus, it coincides with the radius-vector of the center of mass of the whole system.

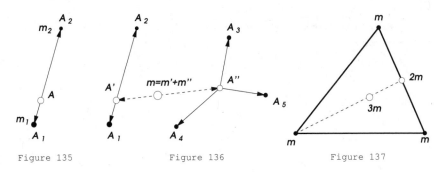

Figure 135   Figure 136   Figure 137

Example. Equip each vertex of a given triangle with the same mass m (Figure 137) and compute the center of mass for vertices of one of the sides first. It lies at the midpoint of that side and carries the mass $2m$. By the theorem, the center of mass of the whole system lies on the median connecting this midpoint with the opposite vertex and divides it in the proportion $2m : m$ counting from the vertex. Since the center of mass is the same regardless of the order of grouping, we derive concurrency of medians once again.

130. Ceva's theorem.

Theorem. *Given a triangle ABC* (Figure 138) *and points A′, B′, and C′ on the sides BC, CA, and AB respectively, the lines AA′, BB′, and CC′ are concurrent if and only if the vertices can be equipped with masses such that A′, B′, C′ become centers of mass of the pairs: B and C, C and A, A and B respectively.*

Suppose A, B, and C are material points, and $A′$, $B′$ and $C′$ are positions of the centers of mass of the pairs B and C, C and A, A and B. Then, by the regrouping property, the center of mass of the whole system lies on each of the segments $AA′$, $BB′$, and $CC′$. Therefore these segments are concurrent.

Conversely, assume that the lines $AA′$, $BB′$, and $CC′$ are concurrent. Assign an arbitrary mass $m_A = m$ to the vertex A, and then assign masses to the vertices B and C so that $C′$ and $B′$ become the centers of mass of the pairs A and B, and A and C respectively, namely:

$$m_B = \frac{AC′}{C′B}m, \quad \text{and} \quad m_C = \frac{AB′}{B′C}m.$$

Then the center of mass of the whole system will lie at the intersection point M of the segments $BB′$ and $CC′$. On the other hand, by regrouping, it must lie on the line connecting the vertex A with the center of mass of the pair B and C. Therefore the center of mass of this pair is located at the intersection point $A′$ of the line AM with the side BC.

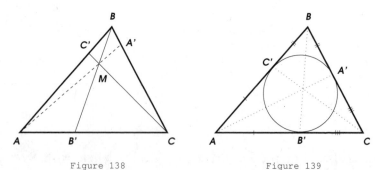

Figure 138   Figure 139

Corollary (Ceva's theorem). *In a triangle ABC, the segments AA′, BB′, and CC′, connecting the vertices with points on the opposite sides, are concurrent if and only if*

$$\frac{AC′}{C′B} \cdot \frac{BA′}{A′C} \cdot \frac{CB′}{B′A} = 1. \tag{$*$}$$

Indeed, when the lines are concurrent, the equality becomes obvious when rewritten in terms of the masses:

$$\frac{m_B}{m_A} \cdot \frac{m_C}{m_B} \cdot \frac{m_A}{m_C} = 1.$$

Conversely, the relation (∗) means that if one assigns masses as in the proof of the theorem, i.e. so that $m_B : m_A = AC' : C'B$ and $m_C : m_A = AB' : B'C$, then the proportion $m_C : m_B = BA' : A'C$ holds too. Therefore all three points C', B', and A' are the centers of mass of the corresponding pairs of vertices. Now the concurrency property is guaranteed by the theorem.

Problem. *In a triangle ABC (Figure 139), let A', B', and C' denote points of tangency of the inscribed circle with the sides. Prove that the lines AA', BB', and CC' are concurrent.*

Solution 1. We have: $AB' = AC'$, $BC' = BA'$, and $CA' = CB'$ (as tangent segments drawn from the vertices to the same circle). Therefore the relation (∗) holds true, and the concurrency follows from the corollary.

Solution 2. Assigning masses $m_A = 1/AB' = 1/AC'$, $m_B = 1/BC' = 1/BA'$, and $m_C = 1/CA' = 1/CB'$, we make A', B', and C' the centers of mass of the corresponding pairs of vertices, and therefore the concurrency follows from the theorem.

131. Menelaus' theorem.

Lemma. **Three points A_1, A_2, and A_3 are collinear** (i.e. lie on the same line) **if and only if they can be equipped with non-zero pseudo-masses m_1, m_2, and m_3** (they are allowed therefore to have different signs) **such that**

$$m_1 + m_2 + m_3 = 0, \quad \text{and} \quad m_1\overrightarrow{OA_1} + m_2\overrightarrow{OA_2} + m_3\overrightarrow{OA_3} = \vec{0}.$$

If the points are collinear, then one can make the middle one (let it be called A_3) the center of mass of the points A_1 and A_2 by assigning their masses according to the proportion $m_2 : m_1 = A_1A_3 : A_3A_2$. Then, for any origin O, we have: $m_1\overrightarrow{OA_1} + m_2\overrightarrow{OA_2} - (m_1 + m_2)\overrightarrow{OA_3} = \vec{0}$, i.e. it suffices to put $m_3 = -m_1 - m_2$.

Conversely, if the required pseudo-masses exist, one may assume (changing, if necessary, the signs of all three) that one of them (say, m_3) is negative while the other two are positive. Then $m_3 = -m_1 - m_2$, and the relation $m_1\overrightarrow{OA_1} + m_2\overrightarrow{OA_2} - (m_1 + m_2)\overrightarrow{OA_3} = \vec{0}$ means that A_3 is the position of the center of mass of the pair of material points A_1 and A_2. Thus A_3 lies on the segment A_1A_2.

Corollary (Menelaus' theorem.) *Any points A', B', and C' (Figure 140) lying on the sides BC, CA, and AB respectively of $\triangle ABC$, or on their extensions, are collinear, if and only if*

$$\frac{AC'}{C'B} \cdot \frac{BA'}{A'C} \cdot \frac{CB'}{B'A} = 1.$$

Remark. This relation looks identical to $(*)$, and it may seem puzzling how the same relation can characterize triples of points A', B', C' satisfying two different geometric conditions. In fact in Menelaus' theorem (see Figure 140), either one or all three of the points must lie on extensions of the sides, so that the same relation is applied to two mutually exclusive geometric situations. Furthermore, let us identify the sides of $\triangle ABC$ with number lines by directing them as shown on Figure 140, i.e. the side AB from A to B, BC from B to C, and CA from C to A. Then the segments AC', $C'B$, BA', etc. in the above relation can be understood as signed quantities, i.e. real numbers whose absolute values are equal to the lengths of the segments, and the signs are determined by the directions of the vectors $\overrightarrow{AC'}$, $\overrightarrow{C'B}$, $\overrightarrow{BA'}$, etc. on the respective number lines. With this convention, the correct form of the relation in Menelaus' theorem is:

$$\frac{AC'}{C'B} \cdot \frac{BA'}{A'C} \cdot \frac{CB'}{B'A} = -1, \qquad (**)$$

thereby differing from the relation in Ceva's theorem by the sign.[3]

To prove Menelaus' theorem in this improved formulation, note that we can always assign to the vertices A, B, and C some real numbers a, b, and c so that C' (resp. B') becomes the center of mass of the pair of points A and B (resp. C and A) equipped with pseudo-masses a and $-b$ (resp. c and $-a$). Namely, it suffices to take: $-b : a = AC' : C'B$ and $-a : c = CB' : B'A$. Then the relation $(**)$ means that $BA' : A'C = -c : b$, i.e. A' is the center of mass of the pair B and C equipped with pseudo-masses b and $-c$ respectively. Thus, we have: $(a-b)\overrightarrow{OC'} = a\overrightarrow{OA} - b\overrightarrow{OB}$, $(c-a)\overrightarrow{OB'} = c\overrightarrow{OC} - a\overrightarrow{OA}$, and $(b-c)\overrightarrow{OA'} = b\overrightarrow{OB} - c\overrightarrow{OC}$. Adding these equalities, and putting $m_A = b - c$, $m_B = c - a$, $m_C = a - b$, we find:

$$m_A\overrightarrow{OA'} + m_B\overrightarrow{OB'} + m_C\overrightarrow{OC'} = \vec{0}, \quad m_A + m_B + m_C = 0.$$

---

[3]In Ceva's theorem, it is also possible to apply the sign convention and consider points on the extensions of the sides. Then the relation $(*)$ remains the correct criterion for the three lines to be concurrent (or parallel). When $(*)$ holds, an even number (i.e. 0 or 2) of the points lie on the extensions of the sides.

Therefore the points A', B', and C' are collinear.

Conversely, for any points C' and B' in the interior or on the extensions of the sides AB and CA, we can find a point A' on the line BC such that the relation (**) holds true. Then, according to the previous argument, points A', B', and C' are collinear, i.e. point A' must coincide with the point of intersection of the lines $B'C'$ and BC. Thus the relation (**) holds true for any three collinear points on the sides of a triangle or on their extensions.

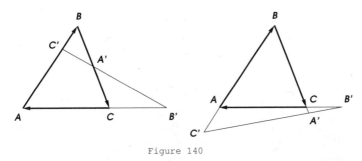

Figure 140

132. The method of barycenters demystified. This method, developed and applied in §§128–131 to some problems of *plane* geometry, can be explained using geometry of vectors in *space*.

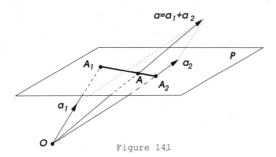

Figure 141

Position the plane P in space in such a way (Figure 141) that it misses the point O chosen for the origin. Then, to each point A on the plane, one can associate a line in space passing through the origin, namely the line OA. When the point comes equipped with a mass (or pseudo-mass) m, we associate to this material point on the plane the vector $\vec{a} = m\overrightarrow{OA}$ in space. We claim that this way, *the center of mass of a system of material points on the plane corresponds to the sum of the vectors associated to them in space*. Indeed, if A denotes the center of mass of a system of n material points A_1, ..., A_n in the plane of masses m_1, ..., m_n, then the total mass is equal to

$m = m_1 + \cdots + m_n$, and the corresponding vector in space is

$$\vec{a} = m\overrightarrow{OM} = m_1\overrightarrow{OA_1} + \cdots + m_n\overrightarrow{OA_n} = \vec{a_1} + \cdots + \vec{a_n}.$$

In particular, the regrouping property of the center of mass follows from associativity of the addition of vectors.

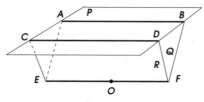

Figure 142

Remark. The above method of associating lines passing through the origin to points of the plane P turns out to be fruitful and leads to the so-called **projective geometry**. In projective geometry, beside ordinary points of the plane P, there exist "points at infinity." They correspond to lines passing through the origin and parallel to P (e.g. EF on Figure 142). Moreover, lines on the plane P (e.g. AB or CD) correspond to planes (Q or R) passing through the origin. When $AB \| CD$, the lines do not intersect on the plane P, but in projective geometry they intersect "at infinity," namely at the "point" corresponding to the line EF of intersection of the planes Q and R. Thus, the optical illusion that two parallel rails of a railroad track meet at the line of the horizon becomes reality in projective geometry.

EXERCISES

251. In the plane, let A, B, C, D, E be arbitrary points. Construct the point O such that $\overrightarrow{OA} + \overrightarrow{OB} + \overrightarrow{OC} = \overrightarrow{OD} + \overrightarrow{OE}$.

252.* In a circle, three non-intersecting chords AB, CD, and EF are given, each congruent to the radius of the circle, and the midpoints of the segments BC, DE, and FA are connected. Prove that the resulting triangle is equilateral.

253. Prove that if a polygon has several axes of symmetry, then they are concurrent.

254. Prove that the three segments connecting the midpoints of opposite edges of a tetrahedron bisect each other.

255. Prove that bisectors of exterior angles of a triangle meet extensions of the opposite sides at collinear points.

256. Formulate and prove an analogue of the previous problem for bisectors of one exterior and two interior angles of a triangle.

257. Prove that if vertices of a triangle are equipped with masses proportional to the opposite sides, then the center of mass coincides with the incenter.

258.* Prove that tangents to a circle at the vertices of an inscribed triangle intersect extensions of the opposite sides at collinear points.

259. In the plane, three circles of different radii are given outside each other, and for each pair, the external common tangents are drawn up to their intersection point. Prove that the three intersection points are collinear.

260. In the plane, three pairwise disjoint circles are given outside each other, and for each pair, the intersection point of internal common tangents is constructed. Prove that the three lines, connecting each intersection point with the center of the remaining circle, are concurrent.

261. Prove the following reformulation of Ceva's theorem: On the sides BC, CA, and AB of $\triangle ABC$ (Figure 138), three points A', B', and C' are chosen. Prove that the lines AA', BB', and CC' are concurrent if and only if

$$\frac{\sin \angle ACC'}{\sin \angle C'CB} \frac{\sin \angle BAA'}{\sin \angle A'AC} \frac{\sin \angle CBB'}{\sin \angle B'BA} = 1.$$

262. Give a similar reformulation of Menelaus' theorem.

263. Two triangles ABC and $A'B'C'$ are given in the plane, and through the vertices of each of them, lines parallel to the respective sides of the other are drawn. Prove that if the lines of one of the triples are concurrent, then the lines of the other triple are concurrent too.

264.* Prove **Pappus' theorem**: If points A, B, C lie on one line, and A', B', C' on another, then the three intersection points of the lines AB' and BA', BC' and CB', AC' and CA', are collinear.
Hint: Reduce to the case of parallel lines using projective geometry, i.e. by restating the problem about points and lines in the plane in terms of corresponding lines and planes in space.

265.* Prove **Desargues' theorem**: In the plane, if the lines AA', BB', and CC' connecting vertices of two triangles ABC and $A'B'C'$ are concurrent, then the three intersection points of each pair of extended respective sides (i.e. AB and $A'B'$, BC and $B'C'$, and CA and $C'A'$) are collinear, and *vice versa*.
Hint: Represent the diagram as a projection from space.

3 Foundations of geometry

133. Euclid's "Elements." Many theorems of geometry can be not only proved by way of reasoning, but also confirmed by direct observation. This intuitive, visual nature of geometry allows one to discover many geometric facts long before they can be rigorously justified. The ancient Egyptians (at about 2000 B.C.) were using this empirical method of establishing the simplest geometric results needed for practical purposes. However, self-evidence of conclusions, derived by observing diagrams, can be deceptive, especially when the diagrams become complicated.

The ancient Greeks, who inherited elements of mathematical culture from the Egyptians, generalized their observations and developed more reliable forms of reasoning. All geometric results were now confirmed by flawless logical arguments relying only on explicitly made assumptions about diagrams, thus rendering the conclusions independent of accidental details of specific diagrams. Around 300 B.C., a Greek geometer **Euclid** gave a systematic exposition of basic geometric knowledge of his time in a series of 13 books under the common title *Elements*. This work laid down foundations of the mathematical method and remains, even by the standards of modern science, a quite satisfactory account of elementary geometry.

Euclid's exposition begins with **definitions**, **postulates**, and **common notions** (also known as **axioms**). Here are the first seven of the 23 definitions (in the English translation [1]):

*1. A **point** is that which has no part.*
*2. A **line** is a breadthless length.*
3. The extremities of a line are points.
*4. A **straight line** is a line that lies evenly with the points on itself.*
*5. A **surface** is that which has length and breadth only.*
6. The extremities of a surface are lines.
*7. A **plane surface** is a surface which lies evenly with the straight lines on itself.*

Then there follow definitions of angles, circles, polygons, triangles, quadrilaterals, parallel and perpendicular lines, etc.

There are five "common notions" about arbitrary quantities:

1. Things which are equal to the same thing are also equal to one another.
2. If equals be added to equals, the wholes are equal.
3. If equals be subtracted from equals, then the remainders are equal.
4. Things which coincide with one another are equal to one another.
5. The whole is greater than the part.

The postulates bear specifically geometric content:

Let the following be postulated:
1. To draw a straight line from any point to any point.
2. To produce a finite straight line continuously in a straight line.
3. To describe a circle with any center and distance.
4. That all right angles are equal[4] to one another.
5. That, if a straight line falling onto two straight lines make the interior angles on the same side less than two right angles, the two straight lines, if produced indefinitely, meet on that side on which are the angles less than the two right angles.

Then Euclid proceeds to stating geometric **propositions**, one after another, and deriving them logically, using the definitions, axioms, postulates and previously proved propositions (pretty much the way we do it in this book).[5]

134. Non-Euclidean geometry. From the modern point of view, logical foundations of elementary geometry, in the form we inherited them from Euclid, are not free of defects.

One is the failure to acknowledge explicitly a number of implicit assumptions used in our arguments. For instance, the definition of **congruent figures** assumes the possibility of moving geometric figures in space as solid objects.

Another one is the vague character of basic definitions, which do not really tell us what points, lines, and planes *are*, but merely explain in what direction the everyday meaning of these words becomes idealized in mathematics.[6]

Historically, the need for more solid logical foundations of geometry emerged as a result of the discovery in the early 19th century of **non-Euclidean geometries**, i.e. consistent geometric theories where Euclid's **5th postulate** does not hold true. As it was discussed in Book I, §§75–78, the 5th postulate is equivalent to the **parallel postulate**: *Through every point not lying on a given line, a line parallel to the given one can be drawn, and such a line is unique.*

---

[4] *congruent* in our terminology

[5] A notable distinction however is that Euclid's discourse is more conservative than ours: he does not allow himself even to *talk* about a certain diagram if it was not shown beforehand how to *construct* this diagram. This explains the role and scope of the first three postulates, which merely decree that it is *possible* to draw a line through two points, to extend a segment, and to draw a circle of arbitrary center and radius.

[6] Historians still argue about the role attributed by Euclid to his first definitions. E.g. according to [3], they originally formed an unstructured succession of sentences, which became separated and numbered only in later translations.

In 1820–1830, two geometers: Russian **Nikolai Lobachevsky** and Hungarian **János Bolyai**, showed independently that there exist geometric theories where the parallel postulate is replaced by its negation, and which are just as rich in content as the classical Euclidean geometry. They arrived at this result by trying (as did many others before them) to derive the 5th postulate from the remaining ones, but were the first to realize that such derivation is impossible.

135. Hilbert's axioms. In 1899, David Hilbert gave the first fully rigorous account [2] of foundations of elementary geometry, both Euclidean and non-Euclidean.

It is inevitable, that by attempting to accurately define all concepts in terms of previously defined ones, and those in terms of even earlier defined concepts, one will sooner or later run out of those "previously defined," and end up with a collection of **undefinable notions**, whose meaning can be conveyed only intuitively.

Hilbert chooses *points, lines,* and *planes* to be the undefinable notions of geometry. Furthermore, he assumes that these geometric objects can be (or not) in certain **relations** with each other, namely:

a point can lie on a line, a point can lie on a plane, a line can lie on a plane, a point can **lie between** *two other points lying on a given line,* (note that using these relations, one can formulate definitions of segments, angles, etc.), and *two given segments (or angles) can be congruent to each other.*

One can try to interpret these notions and relations in the usual intuitive way, but the whole point of Hilbert's axiomatic approach is that such interpretations are considered irrelevant. The meaning and properties of the notions and relations are established by a certain list of *axioms*. All further geometric propositions are obtained from the axioms by logical derivation, which in principle can be done formally, not appealing to the nature of the objects involved. By the expression of Hilbert himself, "it must be possible to replace in all geometric statements the words *point, line, plane* by *table, chair, mug.*" To illustrate the character of Hilbert's axioms, we list the three **axioms of order**:

(i) *If the points A, B, C lie on a line, and B lies between A and C, then B lies also between C and A.*

(ii) *If A and C are two points of a line, then there exists at least one point B lying between A and C, and at least one point D such that C lies between A and D.*

(iii) *Of any three points lying on a line, there is always one and only one which lies between the other two.*

We are not going to present here the whole system of Hilbert's 20 axioms; let us mention only that it includes the parallel postulate (or a negation of it), **Archimedes' axiom** (see Book I, §145), and as the last item in the list, the **axiom of completeness**:

To a system of points, lines, and planes, it is impossible to add other elements in such a manner that the system thus generalized forms a new geometry obeying all of the previous axioms.

136. The set-theoretic approach. While Hilbert's work laid down a new area of mathematics: mathematical logic, the modern approach to geometry relies on a different foundation, which strikes a better balance between rigor and intuition. It was proposed in 1916 by **Hermann Weyl** and is based on the algebraic notion of a *vector space.*

What makes Weyl's approach particularly attractive is that it uses only very general undefinable notions, such as *sets* and *elements*, which permeate all of mathematics, and not only geometry. Set theory first emerged at the end of the 19th century in the work of a German mathematician **Georg Cantor** as the theory comparing various infinite sets, but soon became the universal language of modern mathematics.

Sets are thought of as collections of objects of any nature. It may be impossible to express this more formally than by saying that a **set** is considered given if for every object it is specified whether it is an **element** of this set or not. All further notions are introduced on the basis of this relation between elements and sets. For example, one set is called a **subset** of another, if every element of the first set is also an element of the second.

So far, following Euclid, we considered lines and planes as separate entities, and not merely as sets of points lying on them.[7] One simplifying distinction of the set-theoretic approach to geometry is that only the set of points and its properties need to be postulated, while lines and planes are defined simply as certain subsets of the set of points, so that all their properties become theorems.

Another ingredient of Weyl's approach to geometry is the **set R of real numbers** (positive, zero, and negative) endowed with the usual operations of addition, subtraction, multiplication, and division by non-zero numbers. To define real numbers and the arithmetic operations, it suffices to introduce them in terms of signed sequences of decimal numerals (as outlined in Book I, §§151–153).

---

[7]In particular, the same line could be represented by any finite piece of it (that fits a diagram), and it made sense to talk about "extending" the line.

137. Axioms of a vector space. By definition, a **vector space** is a set, equipped with operations of **addition** and **multiplication by scalars** which are required to satisfy certain **axioms**. The set will be denoted here by $\mathcal{V}$, and its elements will be referred to as **vectors**. The scalars form the set **R** of real numbers, which includes therefore the numbers 0 and 1. To every vector $\vec{v}$ and scalar α (i.e. any elements of the sets $\mathcal{V}$ and **R**), the operation of multiplication associates a new vector, denoted $\alpha\vec{v}$. To every pair of vectors $\vec{u}$ and $\vec{v}$, the operation of addition associates a new vector denoted $\vec{u} + \vec{v}$. The axioms require that for all vectors $\vec{u}, \vec{v}, \vec{w}$ and all scalars α, β the following holds true:

(i) $$(\vec{u} + \vec{v}) + \vec{w} = \vec{u} + (\vec{v} + \vec{w}),$$
(ii) $$\vec{u} + \vec{v} = \vec{v} + \vec{u},$$
(iii) *There is a unique vector* $\vec{0}$ *such that* $\vec{u} + \vec{0} = \vec{u}$ *for all* $\vec{u}$,
(iv) $$\alpha(\beta\vec{u}) = (\alpha\beta)\vec{u}$$
(v) $$\alpha(\vec{u} + \vec{v}) = \alpha\vec{u} + \alpha\vec{v},$$
(vi) $$(\alpha + \beta)\vec{u} = \alpha\vec{u} + \beta\vec{u},$$
(vii) $$0\vec{u} = \vec{0},$$
(viii) $$1\vec{u} = \vec{u}.$$

In words, the axioms express: associativity and commutativity of addition of vectors, existence and uniqueness of the zero vector, associativity of multiplication by scalars, its distributivity with respect to addition of vectors, to addition of scalars, and the way the multiplication by the scalars 0 and 1 acts.

Here is an example of explicit derivation from the axioms.

For every vector $\vec{u}$ *there exists a unique* **opposite vector**, *i.e. a vector* $\vec{v}$ *such that* $\vec{u} + \vec{v} = \vec{0}$.

Indeed, we have:

$\vec{0} = 0\vec{u} = (1 + (-1))\vec{u}$ (vii), and $0 = 1 + (-1)$
$= 1\vec{u} + (-1)\vec{u} = \vec{u} + (-1)\vec{u},$ (vi) and (viii)
and hence $(-1)\vec{u}$ is opposite to $\vec{u}$.   definition of opposite vectors
Conversely, if $\vec{0} = \vec{u} + \vec{v}$, then   definition of opposite vectors
$(-1)\vec{u} + \vec{0} = (-1)\vec{u} + (\vec{u} + \vec{v}),$ adding each side to $(-1)\vec{u}$
$(-1)\vec{u} = ((-1)\vec{u} + \vec{u}) + \vec{v}$ (iii) and (i)
$= (-1 + 1)\vec{u} + \vec{v} = 0\vec{u} + \vec{v} = \vec{0} + \vec{v}$ (vi), $-1 + 1 = 0$, and (vii)
$= \vec{v} + \vec{0} = \vec{v}$, i.e. $\vec{v} = (-1)\vec{u}$.   (ii) and (iii)

We will denote the vector opposite to a vector $\vec{u}$ simply by $-\vec{u}$ and write $\vec{w} - \vec{u}$ instead of $\vec{w} + (-\vec{u})$. Due to the axiom (i) we can also write sums of several vectors without parentheses, e.g. $\vec{u} + \vec{v} + \vec{w}$.

138. Subspaces and dimension. Several vectors $\vec{u}, \vec{v}, \ldots, \vec{w}$ are called **linearly dependent** if there exist scalars $\alpha, \beta, \ldots, \gamma$, not all equal to 0, such that

$$\alpha\vec{u} + \beta\vec{v} + \cdots + \gamma\vec{w} = \vec{0}.$$

The vectors are called **linearly independent** otherwise, i.e. if this equality is possible only when $\alpha = \beta = \cdots = \gamma = 0$. Clearly, including new elements in a linearly dependent set of vectors leaves it linearly dependent. A vector space is said to be of **dimension** k if it contains a set of k linearly independent vectors, but every $k+1$ vectors are linearly dependent.

An expression of the form

$$\alpha\vec{u} + \beta\vec{v} + \cdots + \gamma\vec{w}$$

is called a **linear combination** of vectors $\vec{u}, \vec{v}, \ldots, \vec{w}$ with coefficients $\alpha, \beta, \ldots, \gamma$. Given a set of vectors in a vector space $\mathcal{V}$, all linear combinations of these vectors form a **subspace** $\mathcal{W}$, i.e. a subset of $\mathcal{V}$ which is a vector space on its own with respect to the same operations. Indeed, sums and scalar multiples of linear combinations of given vectors are themselves linear combinations of the same vectors. The same applies to the opposites of such linear combinations, and to the vector $\vec{0} = 0\vec{u} + 0\vec{v} + \cdots + 0\vec{w}$, which therefore lie in $\mathcal{W}$. Thus the operations with vectors are well-defined in $\mathcal{W}$, and satisfy axioms (i)–(viii) because the axioms hold true in the ambient vector space $\mathcal{V}$.

Theorem. (1) *All scalar multiples of a single non-zero vector form a subspace of dimension 1.*

(2) *All linear combinations of two linearly independent vectors form a subspace of dimension 2.*

(1) Indeed, a nonzero vector $\vec{u}$ forms a linearly independent set consisting of one element, while any two scalar multiples $\vec{a} = \alpha\vec{u}$ and $\vec{b} = \beta\vec{u}$ of $\vec{u}$ are linearly dependent. Indeed, if $\beta = 0$, then $0\vec{a} + 1\vec{b} = \vec{0}$, and if $\beta \neq 0$, then $1\vec{a} - (\alpha/\beta)\vec{b} = \vec{0}$.

(2) To prove that all linear combinations of two linearly independent vectors $\vec{u}$ and $\vec{v}$ form a subspace of dimension 2, it suffices to show that any three such linear combinations: $\vec{a} = \alpha_1\vec{u} + \alpha_2\vec{v}$, $\vec{b} = \beta_1\vec{u} + \beta_2\vec{v}$, and $\vec{c} = \gamma_1\vec{u} + \gamma_2\vec{v}$ are linearly dependent. Indeed, if $\vec{c} = \vec{0}$, then $0\vec{a} + 0\vec{b} + 1\vec{c} = \vec{0}$, and hence the vectors are linearly dependent. Suppose that $\vec{c} \neq \vec{0}$. Then at least one of the coefficients γ_1, γ_2 is non-zero. For certainty, let $\gamma_2 \neq 0$. Then the vectors

$\vec{a}' = \vec{a} - (\alpha_2/\gamma_2)\vec{c}$ and $\vec{b}' = \vec{b} - (\beta_2/\gamma_2)\vec{c}$ are scalar multiples of a single vector, $\vec{u}$. Therefore the vectors $\vec{a}'$ and $\vec{b}'$ are linearly dependent, i.e. one can find some scalars α and β, not both equal to 0, such that $\alpha\vec{a}' + \beta\vec{b}' = \vec{0}$. Thus

$$\alpha\vec{a} + \beta\vec{b} - \left(\alpha\frac{\alpha_2}{\gamma_2} + \beta\frac{\beta_2}{\gamma_2} \right)\vec{c} = \vec{0},$$

and hence the vectors $\vec{a}$, $\vec{b}$, and $\vec{c}$ are linearly dependent.

    Remark. One can show that all linear combinations of three linearly independent vectors form a subspace of dimension 3, etc.

    139. Points, lines and planes. The set of **points** of solid Euclidean geometry is defined as a vector space $\mathcal{V}$ of dimension 3. The latter condition can be considered as an extra axiom, the **axiom of dimension**:

There exist three linearly independent vectors, but any four vectors are linearly dependent.

    The set of points comes equipped therefore with a distinguished point, the **origin** O, corresponding to the vector $\vec{0}$. To an arbitrary point U, there corresponds a vector $\vec{u}$, called its **radius-vector**. We will continue using the notation $\overrightarrow{UV}$ for the vector $\vec{v} - \vec{u}$.

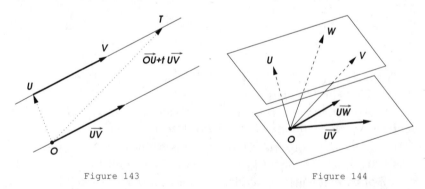

Figure 143   Figure 144

    Subspaces of dimension 1 and 2 are examples of lines and planes of solid geometry, namely those lines and planes that pass through the origin O. By definition, an arbitrary line (or plane), not necessarily passing through the origin, is obtained from a subspace of dimension 1 (respectively 2) by **translation**, i.e. by adding a fixed vector ($\overrightarrow{OU}$, Figures 143 and 144) to all vectors of that subspace. In other words, a subset of $\mathcal{V}$ is called a **line** (respectively **plane**) if the differences

$(\overrightarrow{OV} - \overrightarrow{OU} = \overrightarrow{UV}$, Figures 143 and 145) of radius-vectors of its points form a subspace of dimension 1 (respectively 2).

The following result shows how Euclid's postulates about lines and planes become theorems under the vector approach to foundations of solid geometry.

Theorem. (1) *For every two distinct points, there is a unique line passing through them.*

(2) *For every three points not lying on the same line, there exists a unique plane passing through them.*

(3) *If two points of a given line lie in a given plane, then every point of the line lies in that plane.*

(4) *If two distinct planes have a common point, then they intersect in a line passing through that point.*

(5) *Given a line, and a point not lying on it, there exists a unique line passing through this point and parallel to the given line.*

(1) Given two distinct points U and V (Figure 143), the set of points with the radius-vectors $\overrightarrow{OU} + t\overrightarrow{UV}$, where t is an arbitrary real number, contains U (for $t = 0$), V (for $t = 1$), and forms a line, since all differences of such vectors are scalar multiples of the vector $\overrightarrow{UV}$. Conversely, if a point T lies on any line passing through U and V, then the vector $\overrightarrow{UT}$ must be proportional to $\overrightarrow{UV}$, i.e. $\overrightarrow{UT} = t\overrightarrow{UV}$ for some real number t. Therefore $\overrightarrow{OT} = \overrightarrow{OU} + t\overrightarrow{UV}$, i.e. the point T lies on the line previously described.

(2) If three given points U, V, and W (Figure 144) are non-collinear, then the vectors $\overrightarrow{UV}$ and $\overrightarrow{UW}$ are linearly independent. The set of points with the radius-vectors $\overrightarrow{OU} + x\overrightarrow{UV} + y\overrightarrow{UW}$, where x and y are arbitrary real numbers, contains the three given points (take the pair (x, y) to be $(0,0)$, $(1,0)$ and $(0,1)$) and forms a plane. Indeed, differences of such radius-vectors have the form $\alpha\overrightarrow{UV} + \beta\overrightarrow{UW}$ and thus form a subspace of dimension 2. Conversely, if T is any point on a plane passing through U, V, and W, then the three vectors $\overrightarrow{UT}$, $\overrightarrow{UV}$, and $\overrightarrow{UW}$ must lie in the same subspace of dimension 2. Therefore they are linearly dependent, and hence $\overrightarrow{UT} = x\overrightarrow{UV} + y\overrightarrow{UW}$ for some real numbers x and y. Thus $\overrightarrow{OT} = \overrightarrow{OU} + x\overrightarrow{UV} + y\overrightarrow{UW}$, i.e. the point T lies on the plane previously described.

(3) Let $\mathcal{P}$ (Figure 145) be a subspace of dimension 2, and let U and V be distinct points on a plane P obtained from $\mathcal{P}$ by translation. Then the vector $\overrightarrow{UV} = \overrightarrow{OV} - \overrightarrow{OU}$ lies in $\mathcal{P}$, as well as $t\overrightarrow{UV}$ where

t is any real number. Therefore all points with the radius-vectors $\overrightarrow{OU} + t\overrightarrow{UV}$ lie on the plane P.

(4) Suppose that two planes P and P' (Figure 146) intersect at a point U. In the plane P (respectively P'), pick two points V and W (respectively V' and W') not collinear with U. Then the vectors $\overrightarrow{UV}$ and $\overrightarrow{UW}$ (respectively $\overrightarrow{UV'}$ and $\overrightarrow{UW'}$) are linearly independent. Since the space $\mathcal{V}$ has dimension 3, the four vectors are linearly dependent. Therefore there exist real numbers $\alpha, \beta, \alpha', \beta'$ not all equal to 0 such that $\alpha\overrightarrow{UV} + \beta\overrightarrow{UW} = \alpha'\overrightarrow{UV'} + \beta'\overrightarrow{UW'}$. Denote by $\vec{a}$ the vector represented by either of the equal expressions. The point A with the radius-vector $\overrightarrow{OA} = \overrightarrow{OU} + \vec{a}$ lies in both planes. It is different from U, because otherwise we would have $\vec{a} = \vec{0}$ in contradiction with linear independence of each pair of vectors. By (3), the planes intersect along the whole line UA. Any common point B of the planes P and P' must lie on this line. Indeed, otherwise we would have three non-collinear points U, A and B lying in two distinct planes, which contradicts (2).

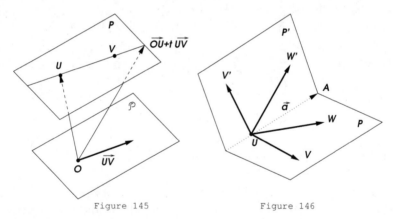

Figure 145   Figure 146

(5) Let UV (Figure 147) be a given line and W a point not lying on it. The plane passing through U, V, and W consists of all points whose radius-vectors have the form $\overrightarrow{OU} + x\overrightarrow{UV} + y\overrightarrow{UW}$. Taking $y = 1$ we see that the plane contains the line formed by points with the radius-vectors $\overrightarrow{OW} + x\overrightarrow{UV}$. It passes through W (when $x = 0$), and does not intersect the line UV. For if it did, the intersection point would have the radius-vector $\overrightarrow{OW} + x\overrightarrow{UV} = \overrightarrow{OU} + t\overrightarrow{UV}$. This would imply: $\overrightarrow{UW} = (t - x)\overrightarrow{UV}$, i.e. that the point W lies on the line UV, which is impossible. Thus, we have found a line passing

through W and parallel to the line UV.

To prove uniqueness, consider any line WZ parallel to UV. Since the points U, V, Z, and W lie in the same plane, the three difference vectors $\overrightarrow{UV}$, $\overrightarrow{UW}$, and $\overrightarrow{WZ}$ must be linearly dependent, i.e. $\alpha\overrightarrow{UV} + \beta\overrightarrow{UW} + \gamma\overrightarrow{WZ} = \vec{0}$ for some scalars α, β, γ not all equal to zero. If $\beta \neq 0$, then $\overrightarrow{UW} + (\gamma/\beta)\overrightarrow{WZ} = -(\alpha/\beta)\overrightarrow{UV}$. Adding $\overrightarrow{OU}$ to both sides, we find a point with the radius-vector $\overrightarrow{OW} + (\gamma/\beta)\overrightarrow{WZ} = \overrightarrow{OU} - (\alpha/\beta)\overrightarrow{UV}$, which therefore lies on both parallel lines WZ and UV. Since this is impossible, we conclude that $\beta = 0$. This implies that the vectors $\overrightarrow{UV}$ and $\overrightarrow{WZ}$ are scalar multiples of each other: $\overrightarrow{WZ} = x\overrightarrow{UV}$. Thus $\overrightarrow{OZ} = \overrightarrow{OW} + x\overrightarrow{UV}$, i.e. the line WZ parallel to UV coincides with the line previously constructed.

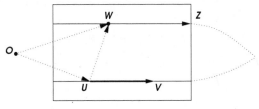

Figure 147

140. Inner products. The concept of a vector space (satisfying the axiom of dimension) is sufficient to describe the set of points, as well as lines and planes, of Euclidean geometry. To introduce measures of lengths and angles, an extra datum is required.

An **inner product** on a vector space $\mathcal{V}$ is an operation that, to every pair of vectors $\vec{u}$ and $\vec{v}$, assigns a real number, denoted $\vec{u} \cdot \vec{v}$, in such a way that the properties of **symmetricity** and **bilinearity** are satisfied: for all vectors $\vec{u}, \vec{v}, \vec{w}$ and scalars α, β

$$\vec{u} \cdot \vec{v} = \vec{v} \cdot \vec{u},$$
$$(\alpha\vec{u} + \beta\vec{v}) \cdot \vec{w} = \alpha(\vec{u} \cdot \vec{w}) + \beta(\vec{v} \cdot \vec{w}).$$

An inner product is called **Euclidean** if $\vec{u} \cdot \vec{u} > 0$ for every non-zero vector $\vec{u}$. A vector space endowed with a Euclidean inner product is called a **Euclidean vector space**.

In a Euclidean vector space, lengths of vectors are defined as

$$|\vec{u}| = \sqrt{\vec{u} \cdot \vec{u}}.$$

This expression makes sense because the number under the square-root sign is non-negative. The distance between two points U and V is then defined as the length $|\overrightarrow{UV}|$ of the difference $\overrightarrow{UV} = \overrightarrow{OV} - \overrightarrow{OU}$ of their radius-vectors.

For a measure of angles from $0°$ to $180°$, the cosine of the angular measure can be taken. The cosine of the angle between two non-zero vectors $\vec{u}$ and $\vec{v}$ is defined by means of the formula:

$$\cos\theta(\vec{u}, \vec{v}) = \frac{\vec{u} \cdot \vec{v}}{|\vec{u}|\,|\vec{v}|}.$$

In order to represent a legitimate value of the cosine, the expression on the R.H.S. needs to lie between -1 and 1. This property is guaranteed by the following **Cauchy–Schwarz inequality**.

Lemma. *For all vectors $\vec{u}$ and $\vec{v}$ of a Euclidean vector space, we have:*

$$(\vec{u} \cdot \vec{v})^2 \leq |\vec{u}|^2\,|\vec{v}|^2,$$

and the equality holds only when the vectors are scalar multiples of each other.

Put $A = \vec{u} \cdot \vec{u} = |\vec{u}|^2$, $B = \vec{u} \cdot \vec{v}$, $C = \vec{v} \cdot \vec{v} = |\vec{v}|^2$, and examine the following expression of degree ≤ 2 with respect to a real number t:

$$(t\vec{u} + \vec{v}) \cdot (t\vec{u} + \vec{v}) = At^2 + 2Bt + C.$$

If t is a solution to the equation $At^2 + 2Bt + C = 0$, then $t\vec{u} + \vec{v} = \vec{0}$ (since non-zero vectors have positive inner squares), and hence one of the vectors is a multiple of the other. If, alternatively, the quadratic equation has no solutions, then (as it is known from algebra) the discriminant $4B^2 - 4AC$ is negative, i.e. $B^2 < AC$ as required.

141. Congruence. A geometric transformation[8] (of the plane) is called an **isometry** if it preserves pairwise distances between points.

One can show (see the last section) that isometries of the Euclidean plane are: translations (by any vector), rotations (through any angle, about any center), reflections (about any line), or **compositions** of these transformations, i.e. the geometric transformations obtained by their consecutive application.

Respectively, one can call two plane geometric figures **congruent** if one of them can be obtained from the other by an isometry of the plane. This definition grounds the concept of congruence on

---

[8]That is, any rule assigning to every point of $\mathcal{V}$ another point of $\mathcal{V}$.

satisfactory foundations. Namely, it makes precise the intuitive idea of "moving figures through space without change" (see Book I, §1).

If applied to space figures, this definition would result in a concept of congruence slightly different from the one used in this book. Indeed, isometries of a Euclidean space of dimension 3 include not only rotations about any axis and translations, but also reflections about any center, or any plane. As a result, geometric figures which are **symmetric** (but not necessarily congruent, see for instance §49) can be obtained from each other by isometries.

EXERCISES

266. From the 5th postulate, derive that if a straight line falling onto two lines makes interior angles on the same side *greater* than two right angles, then the two straight lines, if produced indefinitely, meet on the *other* side to which are the angles greater than two right angles. Deduce the uniqueness statement of the parallel postulate.

267. Show that on the number line, rational numbers form a set of points satisfying Hilbert's axioms of order. Does this set satisfy the axiom of completeness?

268. Show that the requirement in the axiom (iii) of a vector space, that the element $\vec{0}$ is unique, is redundant; namely, it follows from the existence statement of this axiom, and the axiom (ii).

269. Prove that for every vector $\vec{u}$ of a vector space, $\vec{u}+\vec{u}+\vec{u}+\vec{u} = 4\vec{u}$.

270. Prove that the set $\mathbf{R}^k$ of all ordered k-tuples $(x_1,\ldots,x_k)$ of real numbers satisfies the axioms (i)–(viii) of a vector space with respect to the following component-wise operations of multiplication by scalars and addition:

$$\alpha(x_1,\ldots,x_k) = (\alpha x_1,\ldots,\alpha x_k),$$
$$(x_1,\ldots,x_k) + (y_1,\ldots,y_k) = (x_1 + y_1,\ldots,x_k + y_k).$$

271. Can a set of vectors be linearly dependent if it contains only one element?

272. Prove that every subset of a linearly independent set of vectors is linearly independent.

273. Prove that in $\mathbf{R}^k$, the k elements $(1,0,\ldots,0)$, $\ldots$, $(0,\ldots,0,1)$ are linearly independent.

274. Prove that $\mathbf{R}^1$ and $\mathbf{R}^2$ are vector spaces of dimension 1 and 2 respectively.

275.* Give an example of a vector space of infinite dimension, i.e. containing sets of k linearly independent vectors with k as large as one wishes.

276.* Which of the five parts of the theorem in §139 remain true in vector spaces of dimension greater than 3?

277. Prove that planes in space obtained from each other by translation either coincide or do not intersect (i.e. are parallel), and conversely, parallel planes are obtained from each other by translation.

278. Prove that two lines in space obtained from each other by translation either coincide or are parallel (i.e. do not intersect and lie in a plane), and conversely, parallel lines are obtained from each other by translation.

279. Check that the vector space $\mathbf{R}^k$, equipped with the inner product $(x_1, \ldots, x_k) \cdot (y_1, \ldots, y_k) = x_1 y_1 + \cdots + x_k y_k$, is Euclidean, and compute lengths and pairwise angles of the k vectors $(1, 0, \ldots, 0)$, $\ldots$, $(0, \ldots, 0, 1)$.

280. Prove that in a Euclidean vector space, two non-zero vectors are perpendicular if and only if their inner product is equal to zero.

281.* Prove that every Euclidean plane (i.e. a Euclidean vector space of dimension 2) contains two perpendicular vectors of unit length.

282. Prove that in a Euclidean vector space, every set $\vec{e}_1, \ldots, \vec{e}_k$ of non-zero pairwise perpendicular vectors is linearly independent.
Hint: Compute the inner product of their linear combination with each of the vectors.

283.* Prove the **triangle inequality**: for arbitrary radius-vectors $\vec{u}, \vec{v}, \vec{w}$ in a Euclidean vector space, $|\vec{u} - \vec{v}| + |\vec{v} - \vec{w}| \geq |\vec{u} - \vec{w}|$.
Hint: Use the Cauchy–Schwarz inequality.

284. Prove the law of cosines for triangles ABC in a Euclidean vector space: $|\overrightarrow{AB}|^2 + |\overrightarrow{BC}|^2 - 2|\overrightarrow{AB}||\overrightarrow{BC}| \cos \angle ABC = |\overrightarrow{AC}|^2$.

285. Prove that an isometry of a Euclidean vector space preserves angles between any segments, i.e. if it transforms $\triangle ABC$ into $\triangle A'B'C'$, then $\angle ABC = \angle A'B'C'$.

286. Prove that a translation of a Euclidean vector space by a fixed vector $\vec{v}$ (i.e. the transformation assigning to a point $\vec{x}$ the point $\vec{x} + \vec{v}$) is an isometry.

287.* Prove that every geometric transformation of the plane that can be obtained by composing translations, rotations, or reflections, can also be described as the rotation about the origin or reflection about a line passing through the origin, possibly followed by a translation.

4 Introduction to non-Euclidean geometry

142. Coordinates in space. Let $\mathcal{V}$ be a Euclidean vector space of dimension 3. Let $\vec{e}_1$ be a **unit** vector, i.e. any vector of unit length (which can be found by choosing any non-zero vector and dividing it by its length). Take any vector $\vec{u}$ linearly independent of $\vec{e}_1$ and subtract from it a scalar multiple of $\vec{e}_1$ so that the resulting vector $\vec{u} - \alpha\vec{e}_1$ is perpendicular to $\vec{e}_1$. For this, put $\alpha = \vec{u} \cdot \vec{e}_1$ so that

$$(\vec{u} - \alpha\vec{e}_1) \cdot \vec{e}_1 = \vec{u} \cdot \vec{e}_1 - \alpha \, \vec{e}_1 \cdot \vec{e}_1 = \alpha - \alpha = 0.$$

Dividing the resulting vector by its length we obtain a unit vector $\vec{e}_2$ perpendicular to $\vec{e}_1$.

Next, take any vector $\vec{v}$ linearly independent of $\vec{e}_1$ and $\vec{e}_2$. (Such vectors exist because the vector space $\mathcal{V}$ is of dimension > 2.) Subtract from $\vec{v}$ a linear combination of the vectors $\vec{e}_1$ and $\vec{e}_2$ so that the resulting vector $\vec{v} - \alpha_1\vec{e}_1 - \alpha_2\vec{e}_2$ is perpendicular to them. For this, put $\alpha_1 = \vec{v} \cdot \vec{e}_1$, $\alpha_2 = \vec{v} \cdot \vec{e}_2$. Since $\vec{e}_1 \cdot \vec{e}_1 = \vec{e}_2 \cdot \vec{e}_2 = 1$ and $\vec{e}_1 \cdot \vec{e}_2 = 0$, we have:

$$(\vec{v} - \alpha_1\vec{e}_1 - \alpha_2\vec{e}_2) \cdot \vec{e}_1 = \vec{v} \cdot \vec{e}_1 - \alpha_1 \, \vec{e}_1 \cdot \vec{e}_1 - \alpha_2 \, \vec{e}_2 \cdot \vec{e}_1 = 0,$$
$$(\vec{v} - \alpha_1\vec{e}_1 - \alpha_2\vec{e}_2) \cdot \vec{e}_2 = \vec{v} \cdot \vec{e}_1 - \alpha_1 \, \vec{e}_1 \cdot \vec{e}_2 - \alpha_2 \, \vec{e}_1 \cdot \vec{e}_2 = 0.$$

Dividing the resulting vector by its length we obtain a unit vector $\vec{e}_3$ perpendicular to $\vec{e}_1$ and $\vec{e}_2$. In fact we have constructed a **Cartesian coordinate system** in space.

Let $\vec{x}$ be any 4th vector. Since any 4 vectors in a vector space of dimension 3 are linearly dependent, there exist scalars $\alpha_0, \alpha_1, \alpha_2, \alpha_3$ not all equal to 0 such that $\alpha_0\vec{x} = \alpha_1\vec{e}_1 + \alpha_2\vec{e}_2 + \alpha_3\vec{e}_3$. Moreover, $\alpha_0 \neq 0$, since the vectors $\vec{e}_1, \vec{e}_2, \vec{e}_3$ are linearly independent. Dividing this equality by α_0, we find:

$$\vec{x} = x_1\vec{e}_1 + x_2\vec{e}_2 + x_3\vec{e}_3,$$

where x_1, x_2, x_3 are some real numbers. They are called the **coordinates** of the vector $\vec{x}$ with respect to this coordinate system.

The coordinates are uniquely determined by the vector. Indeed, if $\vec{x} = x_1'\vec{e}_1 + x_2'\vec{e}_2 + x_3'\vec{e}_3$, then

$$\vec{0} = \vec{x} - \vec{x} = (x_1 - x_1')\vec{e}_1 + (x_2 - x_2')\vec{e}_2 + (x_3 - x_3')\vec{e}_3,$$

and therefore $x_1 = x_1', x_2 = x_2', x_3 = x_3'$ due to the linear independence of the vectors $\vec{e}_1, \vec{e}_2, \vec{e}_3$.

Furthermore, for every scalar α we have:

$$\alpha\vec{x} = (\alpha x_1)\vec{e}_1 + (\alpha x_2)\vec{e}_2 + (\alpha x_3)\vec{e}_3,$$

i.e. the coordinates of a scalar multiple of a vector are obtained by multiplying the coordinates of the vector by this scalar.

If $\vec{y} = y_1\vec{e}_1 + y_2\vec{e}_2 + y_3\vec{e}_3$ is another vector, then

$$\vec{x} + \vec{y} = (x_1 + y_1)\vec{e}_1 + (x_2 + y_2)\vec{e}_2 + (x_3 + y_3)\vec{e}_3,$$

i.e. the coordinates of the sum of two vectors are obtained by adding corresponding coordinates of the vectors. Since pairwise inner products of the vectors $\vec{e}_1, \vec{e}_3, \vec{e}_3$ are equal to 0, and their inner squares are equal to 1, we find:

$$\vec{x} \cdot \vec{y} = x_1 y_1 + x_2 y_2 + x_3 y_3.$$

These formulas can be generalized. Denote by $\mathbf{R}^k$ the set of all ordered k-tuples $(x_1, \ldots, x_k)$ of real numbers. Introduce in $\mathbf{R}^k$ the operations of multiplication by scalars, addition, and inner product by the formulas:

$$\alpha(x_1, \ldots, x_k) = (\alpha x_1, \ldots, \alpha x_k),$$
$$(x_1, \ldots, x_k) + (y_1, \ldots, y_k) = (x_1 + y_1, \ldots, x_k + y_k),$$
$$(x_1, \ldots, x_k) \cdot (y_1, \ldots, y_k) = x_1 y_1 + \cdots + x_k y_k.$$

It is not hard to verify that the axioms (i)–(viii) of a vector space, as well as the properties of symmetricity and bilinearity of an inner product, are satisfied in $\mathbf{R}^k$. In particular, the k-tuple $(0, \ldots, 0)$ plays the role of the vector $\vec{0}$, and all other k-tuples have positive inner squares: $x_1^2 + \cdots + x_k^2 > 0$. Thus $\mathbf{R}^k$ equipped with these operations is a Euclidean vector space (of dimension k). It is called the **coordinate Euclidean space**. Thus our previous construction of a Cartesian coordinate system in $\mathcal{V}$ establishes the following theorem.

Theorem. *Any Euclidean vector space of dimension 3 can be identified with the coordinate Euclidean space $\mathbf{R}^3$ by associating to each radius-vector the ordered triple of its coordinates with respect to a Cartesian coordinate system.*

Remarks. (1) The same result holds true for a Euclidean space of any finite dimension k, for the plane in particular, where $k = 2$.

(2) The identification of $\mathcal{V}$ with the coordinate Euclidean space is not unique, but depends on the choice of a Cartesian coordinate

system. In other words, if a different triple $\vec{e}_1, \vec{e}_2, \vec{e}_3$ of pairwise perpendicular unit vectors is chosen, the same vector $\vec{x}$ will have a different triple of coordinates with respect to it, and will therefore be assigned a different element of $\mathbf{R}^3$.

(3) We see that within the vector approach to geometry, not only can the foundations be described by a concise and unambiguous set of axioms, but also a *model* satisfying all the axioms can be explicitly constructed. The only datum needed for this is the set $\mathbf{R}$ of real numbers equipped with ordinary arithmetic operations. Moreover, according to the theorem, any such model can be identified with the coordinate one, $\mathbf{R}^3$. In this sense, one can say that solid Euclidean geometry obeying the required axioms exists and is unique.

143. The Klein model. A simple variant of plane geometry that satisfies most of Euclid's (or Hilbert's) axioms but disobeys the parallel postulate was proposed in 1868 by an Italian mathematician **Eugenio Beltrami** and then improved on by the Englishman **Arthur Cayley** and the German **Felix Klein**.

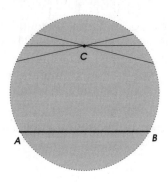

Figure 148

On the Euclidean plane, take any disk, and declare the set of *interior* points of this disk to be the set of *all* points of the Klein model, and chords of the disk to be lines of the Klein model.[9] Then, given a line AB (Figure 148) and a point C outside it, one can draw through C as many lines as one wishes that are parallel to AB in the Klein model (i.e. do not intersect AB inside the disk).

In fact, the Klein model does not yet qualify for the role of a non-Euclidean geometry, because it disobeys not only the parallel postulate, but also some other axioms of Euclidean geometry. Namely, if

---

[9]This proposal goes therefore, although not too far, in the direction (using Hilbert's metaphor) of *table, chair, mug* taking on the role of *point, line, plane*.

we assume that the distance in the Klein model is measured in the usual Euclidean way, then Euclid's 4th postulate (about existence of circles of arbitrary radius with arbitrary centers) no longer holds true. However from Hilbert's point of view, it is the axiom of completeness that fails in the Klein model. Namely, one can enclose the disk of all points of the Klein model into a larger disk and thus get a new Klein model which, compared to the original one, has extra points and lines. We will see later that these defects can be corrected by changing the concept of distance (in such a way that the points of the boundary circle become infinitely far from interior points).

The significance of the Klein model becomes more clear in the context of numerous attempts, known in the history of mathematics, to derive the parallel postulate from the others. Following the method of *reductio ad absurdum*, one would start with the negation of the parallel postulate and try to reach a contradiction.

The Klein model shows that one does not come to a contradiction by merely rejecting the parallel postulate. Moreover, if any argument that makes sense in the Klein model could lead to a contradiction, this would mean that a contradiction is found in the classical plane geometry. This is because the Klein model is described in terms of the classical plane geometry. Thus the plane geometry, where the parallel postulate holds true, cannot be **consistent** (i.e. free of logical contradictions) unless the Klein model, where the parallel postulate fails, is also consistent.

144. Spherical geometry. In the Euclidean space $\mathbf{R}^3$, consider the surface given by the coordinate equation

$$x_1^2 + x_2^2 + x_3^2 = R^2.$$

It consists of all points whose radius-vectors have the length R. It is therefore the sphere of radius R centered at the origin. Geometry on this surface is called **spherical geometry**. It provides an approximation to geometry of the Globe, and a model of non-Euclidean geometry. Namely (Figure 149), one defines *lines* of spherical geometry as great circles of the sphere. Every great circle is obtained by intersecting the sphere by a plane passing through the center. Any two such planes intersect along a line in space passing through the center (O). This line cuts through the sphere at two diametrically opposite points (C and C'), which therefore lie on both great circles. This shows that *in spherical geometry, every two lines intersect.* Thus, the Euclidean parallel postulate fails in spherical geometry, because there are no parallel lines there at all.

The length of a line segment (e.g. AB, Figure 149) in spherical geometry is taken to be the Euclidean arc length of the corresponding arc of the great circle, i.e. $\pi R(\alpha/2d)$, where $2d$ and α are measures of the straight angle and central angle AOB, respectively. Areas of regions in spherical geometry are also defined in the natural way, i.e. as Euclidean areas of the corresponding parts of the sphere (e.g. $4\pi R^2$ for the total area of the sphere). To measure angles on the surface of the sphere, one measures the Euclidean angle $(A'C'B')$ between the rays *tangent* to the corresponding great circles at a point (C') of intersection.

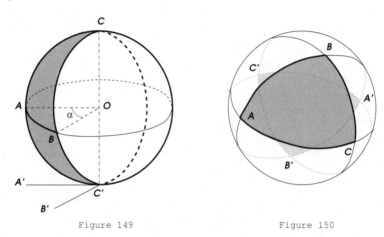

Figure 149 Figure 150

Theorem. *The sum of interior angles of a spherical triangle* $(ABC,$ *Figure 150*$)$ *is greater than* $2d$. *More precisely, the ratio of the sum of the angles* $(\alpha, \beta,$ *and* $\gamma)$ *to the straight angle* $2d$ *exceeds* 1 *by the ratio of the spherical area* S *of the triangle to the area of the great disk:*

$$\frac{\alpha + \beta + \gamma}{2d} = 1 + \frac{S}{\pi R^2}.$$

Firstly, examine a **spherical lune** $(CAC'B,$ shaded on Figure 149) enclosed between two great semicircles. The lune is swept by one of the semicircles rotated about the axis CC' through the angle $\alpha = \angle AOB$. It is clear (see also Remark in §112) that the area of the lune is proportional to the angle of rotation. The area is therefore equal to $4\pi R^2(\alpha/4d) = \pi R^2(\alpha/d)$. The angle $A'C'B'$ between the sides of the lune at the vertex C' is a linear angle of the dihedral angle $ACC'B$ (since the plane $A'C'B'$ is tangent to the sphere at the point C' and is therefore perpendicular to the radius OC'). Thus $\alpha = \angle A'C'B'$. Note that the two great circles CAC' and CBC' divide the sphere into four lunes, one of which is symmetric to the lune $CAC'B$ about the center O of the sphere and has the same area. We conclude that a pair of centrally symmetric lunes with interior angles α at the vertices have the total area $2\pi R^2(\alpha/d)$.

Consider now any three great circles (Figure 150). They divide the sphere into four pairs of centrally symmetric spherical triangles. Let $\triangle ABC$ and $\triangle A'B'C'$ be one of the pairs. The interior spherical angles of these triangles, and the angles vertical to them are at the same time interior angles of three pairs of centrally symmetric lunes (e.g. the pair $ABA'C$ and $AC'A'B'$ of lunes with the vertices A and A'). The total area of these three pairs of lunes is equal to $2\pi R^2(\alpha + \beta + \gamma)/d$, where α, β, γ are the angles of $\triangle ABC$. On the other hand, these three pairs of lunes cover each of the spherical triangles ABC and $A'B'C'$ three times, and the rest of the sphere once. Thus we have:

$$2\pi R^2 \frac{\alpha + \beta + \gamma}{d} = 4\pi R^2 + 4S.$$

Dividing by the total area of the sphere, we obtain the required result.

As a model of non-Euclidean plane, spherical geometry suffers the following obvious flaw: through a pair of centrally symmetric points of the sphere, pass infinitely many great circles (while in plane geometry — Euclidean or not — exactly one line through every pair of points is allowed). This defect is easy to correct: it suffices to declare that *each pair of centrally symmetric points of the sphere represents a single element of the set of points*. This way one obtains the **spherical model** of non-Euclidean geometry, which obeys all but one axiom expected of a geometric plane, namely the parallel postulate, which is replaced with the property that *every two lines meet at exactly one point*. Since the spherical model is constructed entirely in terms of the coordinate Euclidean space $\mathbf{R}^3$, this version of non-Euclidean geometry turns out to be at least as consistent as solid Euclidean geometry.

It is useful to compare the spherical model with the construction, outlined in §132, of the **projective plane**. The set of points of the projective plane can be defined as the set of 1-dimensional subspaces in $\mathbf{R}^3$ (i.e. lines passing through the origin). If we pick in $\mathbf{R}^3$ a plane P (Figure 151) not passing through the origin, those 1-dimensional subspaces (e.g. a) which are not parallel to P intersect P at one point each, and thus can be identified with these points of the plane P.

The projective plane also contains 1-dimensional subspaces parallel to P (e.g. b), which are therefore not represented by points of P (but can be interpreted as its "points at infinity"). Note that each 1-dimensional subspace in $\mathbf{R}^3$ intersects a sphere centered at the origin at a pair of centrally symmetric points (A and A', or B and B'). Thus, the set of points of spherical geometry is identified with the set of points (all — finite or infinite) of the projective plane. This way, the projective plane becomes endowed with notions of distance between points inherited from the sphere, i.e. determined by the angle (AOB) between the 1-dimensional subspaces.

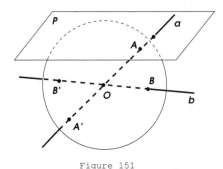 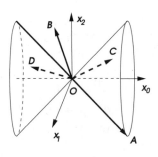

Figure 151   Figure 152

145. The Minkowski space. In the coordinate vector space $\mathbf{R}^3$, introduce the **Minkowski inner product**:

$$(x_0, x_1, x_2) \cdot (y_0, y_2, y_3) = -x_0 y_0 + x_1 y_1 + x_2 y_2.$$

It is straightforward to verify that the symmetricity and bilinearity properties, required of an inner product, are satisfied. However this inner product is not Euclidean, because there exist non-zero vectors $\vec{x} = (x_0, x_1, x_2)$ whose inner square $\vec{x} \cdot \vec{x}$ is zero or even negative. The set of points satisfying $\vec{x} \cdot \vec{x} = 0$ is given by the equation $x_0^2 = x_1^2 + x_2^2$. Fixing a non-zero value of x_0 we obtain a circle on a plane, parallel to the coordinate (x_1, x_2)-plane, with the center lying on the x_0-axis, and radius equal to $|x_0|$. On the other hand, if a point $\vec{x}$ lies on this surface, then all points with the radius-vectors proportional to $\vec{x}$ do too. Thus, $\vec{x} \cdot \vec{x} = 0$ *is a conical surface* (Figure 152) *with the vertex at the origin, obtained by rotating a line* (e.g. OA) *about the x_0-axis*.

The space $\mathbf{R}^3$ equipped with the above inner product is called *Minkowski space* (as opposed to *Euclidean space*), after a German mathematician **Hermann Minkowski** who introduced it in 1908 in connection with Einstein's theory of relativity. Following a physicist's terminology, we call the surface $\vec{x} \cdot \vec{x} = 0$ the **light cone**.[10] It is formed by **light-like** vectors (e.g. $\overrightarrow{OA}$), and separates **space-like** vectors (e.g. $\overrightarrow{OB}$), which satisfy $\vec{x} \cdot \vec{x} > 0$ and lie between the two halves of the cone, from **time-like** vectors (e.g. $\overrightarrow{OC}$ or $\overrightarrow{OD}$), which satisfy $\vec{x} \cdot \vec{x} < 0$ and fill the two interior regions of the cone.

In the **Minkowski space**, subspaces containing no space-like vectors are of dimension 1, and this property distinguishes it from other inner product spaces. Note that the distance

$$\sqrt{\overrightarrow{AB} \cdot \overrightarrow{AB}}$$

between two points A and B in the Minkowski space is well-defined only when the vector $\overrightarrow{AB}$ (Figure 152) is space-like.

Two vectors whose inner product vanishes are called **orthogonal**.

Theorem. *In the Minkowski space, non-zero vectors orthogonal to a time-like vector, are space-like.*

Assume that $\vec{v}$ is a time-like or light-like vector orthogonal to a time-like vector $\vec{u}$, i.e. $\vec{u} \cdot \vec{u} < 0$, $\vec{u} \cdot \vec{v} = 0$, and $\vec{v} \cdot \vec{v} \leq 0$. Then

$$(\alpha\vec{u} + \beta\vec{v}) \cdot (\alpha\vec{u} + \beta\vec{v}) = \alpha^2 \vec{u} \cdot \vec{u} + 2\alpha\beta\vec{u} \cdot \vec{v} + \beta^2 \vec{v} \cdot \vec{v} \leq 0,$$

i.e. the subspace of dimension 2 formed by all linear combinations of $\vec{u}$ and $\vec{v}$ contains no space-like vectors. In Minkowski space, this is impossible, and hence the vector $\vec{v}$ must be space-like.

146. The hyperbolic plane. In the Minkowski space $\mathbf{R}^3$, consider the surface given by the coordinate equation (Figure 153)

$$x_0^2 - x_1^2 - x_2^2 = R^2.$$

It consists of all points whose radius-vectors are time-like and have a fixed Minkowski inner square $\vec{x} \cdot \vec{x} = -R^2$. The cross section of this surface by a plane with a fixed value of x_0 (i.e. plane perpendicular to the x_0-axis) is a circle of radius $\sqrt{x_0^2 - R^2}$ (when $x_0 > R$ or $x_0 < -R$) with the center on the x_0-axis. Thus it is a surface of revolution about the x_0-axis. For a generatrix, the cross section by the plane $x_1 = 0$ (i.e. coordinate (x_0, x_2)-plane) can be taken. This generatrix is a curve, called **hyperbola**, and the whole surface is

---

[10] In space-time $\mathbf{R}^3$, with one time variable x_0 and two spatial coordinates x_1, x_2, trajectories of light particles, issued at the time moment 0 from the origin, form the light cone, provided that the units are chosen in such a way that the light speed is equal to 1.

called a **hyperboloid**. This hyperboloid in the Minkowski space is the counterpart of the sphere in the Euclidean space.

As explained in §144, in the spherical model of non-Euclidean plane geometry, all subspaces of dimension 1 in the Euclidean space $\mathbf{R}^3$ are taken in the role of points. In the **hyperboloid model** of non-Euclidean plane geometry, only *time-like* subspaces of dimension 1 in the Minkowski space $\mathbf{R}^3$ are taken in the role of points. Every such subspace meets each branch of the hyperboloid at exactly one point. Thus, in the hyperboloid model, the set of points can be identified with one of the two branches, e.g. the branch where $x_0 > 0$. We denote this branch by $\mathcal{H}$ and call the **hyperbolic plane**.

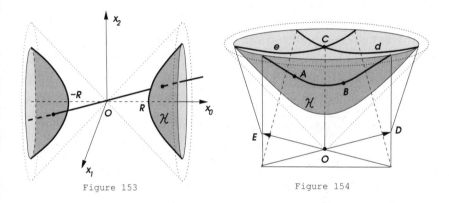

Figure 153   Figure 154

In the hyperbolic model, *lines* are defined by intersecting $\mathcal{H}$ with. subspaces of dimension 2. Pick any two points A and B on the hyperbolic plane $\mathcal{H}$ (Figure 154). In the Minkowski space $\mathbf{R}^3$, there is a unique subspace of dimension 2 containing A and B, namely the plane passing through the points A, B and the origin O. The intersection of this plane with $\mathcal{H}$ is a curve (namely one branch of a hyperbola) which is considered a line of the hyperboloid model. Thus, *in the hyperboloid model of non-Euclidean geometry, one can draw a unique line through every two given points.*

Let C be any point on the hyperbolic plane $\mathcal{H}$ not lying on the line AB, i.e. lying outside the subspace AOB. Inside this subspace, pick any space-like vector $\overrightarrow{OD}$, and draw the plane through the points C, D and O. This plane will intersect the hyperbolic plane $\mathcal{H}$ along a curve d considered a line in the hyperboloid model. This line passes through the point C and does not intersect the line AB. Indeed, the points of intersection of the planes AOB and COD lie on the line OD which is space-like, and therefore does not intersect the hyperboloid.

Picking inside the subspace AOB any space-like vector $\overrightarrow{OE}$ non-proportional to $\overrightarrow{OD}$, and drawing the plane COE, we obtain another line e, which passes through the point C and does not intersect the line AB. Thus, *in the hyperboloid model of non-Euclidean geometry, through every point outside a given line, one can draw more than one line* (in fact infinitely many lines) *parallel to the given one.*

We saw in §143 that the same is true for the Klein model. The hyperboloid model and the Klein model are related as follows. In the Minkowski space (Figure 155), draw a plane perpendicular to the x_0-axis. Every time-like subspace of dimension 1 meets this plane at a point lying in the interior of the disk cut out from the plane by the light cone. Every subspace of dimension 2, containing time-like vectors, intersects the disk along a chord. This way, points and lines of the hyperboloid model correspond to points and lines of the Klein model. We will show below how one can introduce on the hyperbolic plane $\mathcal{H}$ measures of lengths, angles, and areas using geometry of the Minkowski space.

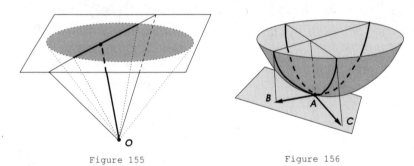

Figure 155   Figure 156

The **angle** between two lines on the hyperbolic plane $\mathcal{H}$ intersecting at a point A (Figure 156) is defined as the angle in the Minkowski space between any non-zero vectors ($\overrightarrow{AB}$ and $\overrightarrow{AC}$) tangent to these lines. The vectors lie in the plane tangent to the hyperboloid at the point A. We will see in §152 that this plane is orthogonal to the radius-vector $\overrightarrow{OA}$ of the point A with respect to the Minkowski inner product. (For instance, the plane tangent to the hyperboloid at the point $(R, 0, 0)$ on Figure 153 is given by the equation $x_0 = R$; all vectors parallel to this plane have the form $(0, u_1, u_2)$ and are therefore orthogonal to the vector $(R, 0, 0)$.) Since the radius-vector $\overrightarrow{OA}$ is time-like, all vectors tangent to the hyperboloid at the point A are space-like (by the theorem of §145). Therefore the inner product on the tangent plane is Euclidean, so that the angle between the vectors $\overrightarrow{AB}$ and $\overrightarrow{AC}$ can be measured in the usual way:

$$\cos \angle BAC = \frac{\overrightarrow{AB} \cdot \overrightarrow{AC}}{\sqrt{\overrightarrow{AB} \cdot \overrightarrow{AB}}\sqrt{\overrightarrow{AC} \cdot \overrightarrow{AC}}}.$$

Lengths of line segments, and areas of triangles (or more general figures) on a hyperbolic plane are introduced by approximating them using broken lines (respectively polyhedral surfaces) in the Minkowski space and passing to certain limits.

Lemma. *If two points A and B lie on the same hyperbolic plane $\mathcal{H}$, then the vector $\overrightarrow{AB}$ in the Minkowski space is space-like, i.e. $\overrightarrow{AB} \cdot \overrightarrow{AB} > 0$.*

The vector $\frac{1}{2}(\overrightarrow{OA}+\overrightarrow{OB})$ is time-like by the property of the cone to contain in its interior the whole segment whose endpoints lie inside. It is orthogonal to the vector $\overrightarrow{AB} = \overrightarrow{OB} - \overrightarrow{OA}$, because

$$(\overrightarrow{OA} + \overrightarrow{OB}) \cdot (\overrightarrow{OB} - \overrightarrow{OA}) = \overrightarrow{OA} \cdot \overrightarrow{OA} - \overrightarrow{OB} \cdot \overrightarrow{OB} = -R^2 + R^2 = 0.$$

By the theorem of §145, the vector $\overrightarrow{AB}$ must be space-like.

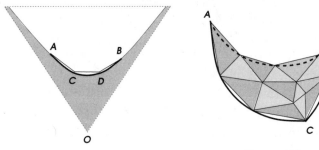

Figure 157   Figure 158

Consider a line on the hyperbolic plane $\mathcal{H}$ obtained by intersecting it with a subspace of dimension 2 in the Minkowski space, and let AB be a segment of this line (i.e. an arc of a hyperbola lying on the section plane, Figure 157). Inscribe into the arc a broken line $ACD \ldots B$. According to the lemma, the segments AC, CD, etc. of this broken line are space-like, and therefore their lengths in the Minkowski space are well-defined. For instance, $|CD| = \sqrt{\overrightarrow{CD} \cdot \overrightarrow{CD}}$. The **length** of the segment AB on the hyperbolic plane is then defined as the limit to which the total length (i.e. $|AC| + |CD| + \cdots$)

of the broken line tends as the maximal length of the individual segments tends to 0 (and therefore the number of segments increases indefinitely).

Likewise, given a triangle on the hyperbolic plane, one can approximate it with a polyhedral surface in the Minkowski space by picking extra points on the sides and in the interior of the triangle and taking them for vertices of the faces (see Figure 158). The areas of the faces are well-defined. (Indeed, their sides are space-like segments according to the lemma, and to compute the area of each face one can use any method of plane Euclidean geometry, e.g. Heron's formula expressing the area of a Euclidean triangle via the lengths of its sides.) Then the **area** of $\triangle ABC$ on the hyperbolic plane is defined as the limit to which the total area of the approximating polyhedral surface in the Minkowski space tends as sizes of edges and faces of the polyhedral surface indefinitely decrease.

The hyperboloid model of non-Euclidean geometry has been constructed entirely in terms of the vector space $\mathbf{R}^3$ and the Minkowski inner product in it. Therefore the geometry of the hyperbolic plane is at least as consistent as the Euclidean and spherical variants. In §152, we will see that (in contrast with spherical geometry) lengths of line segments and areas of triangles on the hyperbolic plane are unbounded. As for the angle sum of a triangle, the following counterpart of the theorem of §144 holds true (although we are not going to prove this).

The sum of interior angles α, β, γ of a triangle on the hyperbolic plane is smaller than $2d$, namely:

$$\frac{\alpha + \beta + \gamma}{2d} = 1 - \frac{S}{\pi R^2},$$

where S is the area of the triangle.

EXERCISES

288. Prove that the coordinates of a vector $\vec{x} = x_1 \vec{e}_1 + x_2 \vec{e}_2 + x_3 \vec{e}_3$ with respect to a Cartesian coordinate system can be computed as the inner products: $x_1 = \vec{x} \cdot \vec{e}_1$, $x_2 = \vec{x} \cdot \vec{e}_2$, $x_3 = \vec{x} \cdot \vec{e}_3$.

289. Verify that the standard inner product in the vector space $\mathbf{R}^k$ is symmetric, bilinear, and Euclidean.

290. Describe all ways to identify a vector space of dimension $k = 1$ with the coordinate space $\mathbf{R}^1$.

291.* Prove that every $k + 1$ elements of $\mathbf{R}^k$ are linearly dependent. **Hint:** Continue the argument used in §138 for $k = 1$ and 2.

292. Prove that the set of points in the coordinate space $\mathbf{R}^3$ satisfying an equation of the form $\alpha_1 x_1 + \alpha_2 x_2 + \alpha_3 x_3 = \beta$, where at least one of the scalars α_i is non-zero, is a plane, perpendicular to the vector $(\alpha_1, \alpha_2, \alpha_3)$. Show that every plane in $\mathbf{R}^3$ can be described by an equation of this form.

293. Which of the **coordinate equations of planes** (introduced in the previous exercise) describe: (a) the same plane? (b) planes passing through the origin? (c) parallel planes?

294. Describe the Klein model of solid geometry.

295. Verify directly the theorem of §144 in the example of a spherical triangle all of whose angles are right.

296. Express the angle sum of a convex spherical polygon in terms of the number n of its vertices, its area S, and the radius R of the sphere.

297. (a) Give an example of a spherical triangle whose exterior angle is smaller than one of the interior angles not adjacent to it.

Remark: Such an example contradicts the theorem of Book I, §42, which comes before the introduction of the parallel postulate, and therefore could be expected to hold true in non-Euclidean geometries.

(b) Examine the proof and determine which assumption, tacitly made in the argument, makes it inapplicable to spherical geometry.

298.* Prove the triangle inequality in spherical geometry.
Hint: See §47.

299. In spherical geometry, find the geometric locus of points equidistant from: (a) a given point; (b) a given line.

300. Show that in a spherical model, the distance between any two points does not exceed a certain constant, and find the maximal possible distance.

301. Show that lines on the projective plane (defined in §132) correspond to lines in the spherical model (defined in §144).

302. Can a non-zero vector be orthogonal to itself?

303. Show that the Minkowski space contains infinitely many subspaces of dimension 2 all of whose non-zero vectors are space-like.

304. Prove that if two points lie on the same half of the light cone, then the distance between them is well-defined.

305. Prove that a directed segment, whose tail lies in the interior of one half of the light cone, and the head in the interior of the other, represents a time-like vector.

5   Isometries

147. Isometries, their inverses, and compositions. We describe all **isometries** of the Euclidean, spherical, and hyperboloid models of plane geometry, i.e. those geometric transformations of the corresponding plane that preserve pairwise distances between points.

Every geometric transformation G that we consider is assumed to be "one-to-one and onto," i.e. it is required to move different points to different ones, and to transform the plane in questions onto the entire plane (rather than a part of it). These assumptions guarantee that the geometric transformation can be *undone*, i.e. that the **inverse** transformation, denoted G^{-1}, is well-defined. Applying one geometric transformation after another we obtain their **composition**. For instance, composing a transformation with its inverse, in either order, we obtain the **identity**, i.e. the transformation which leaves every point in its original place. Obviously, inverses and compositions of isometries are isometries too.

148. Euclidean geometry. Let us begin with the coordinate plane $\mathbf{R}^2$ equipped with the standard Euclidean inner product:

$$(x_1, x_2) \cdot (y_1, y_2) = x_1 y_1 + x_2 y_2.$$

Let (a, b) be any *unit* vector, i.e. $a^2 + b^2 = 1$. Define a geometric transformation Q by the formula:

$$\vec{x} = (x_1, x_2) \mapsto Q\vec{x} = (ax_1 - bx_2, bx_1 + ax_2).$$

This notation means that a point with the radius-vector $\vec{x} = (x_1, x_2)$ on the left of the arrow "$\mapsto$" is moved by Q to a new position whose radius-vector is specified on the right of the arrow.

The transformation Q preserves inner products:

$$Q\vec{x} \cdot Q\vec{y} = (ax_1 - bx_2)(ay_1 - by_2) + (bx_1 + ax_2)(by_1 + ay_2) =$$
$$(a^2 + b^2)x_1 y_1 + (b^2 + a^2)x_2 y_2 + (ba - ab)x_1 y_2 + (ab - ba)x_2 y_1$$
$$= x_1 y_1 + x_2 y_2 = \vec{x} \cdot \vec{y}.$$

Therefore Q preserves distances to the origin and the measure of angles between lines passing through the origin (because the distances and angles are defined using only the inner product). It follows that Q is an isometry:

$$|Q\vec{x} - Q\vec{y}|^2 = |Q\vec{x}|^2 - 2Q\vec{x} \cdot Q\vec{y} + |Q\vec{y}|^2 = |\vec{x}|^2 - 2\vec{x} \cdot \vec{y} + |\vec{y}|^2 = |\vec{x} - \vec{y}|^2.$$

In fact Q is the **rotation** about the origin through the angle θ such that $a = \cos\theta$, $b = \sin\theta$. Indeed, for $\vec{e}_1 = (1,0)$ and $\vec{e}_2 = (0,1)$ (Figure 159), $Q\vec{e}_1 = (a,b)$ and $Q\vec{e}_2 = (-b,a)$, i.e. the vectors are rotated through the angle θ counter-clockwise. Their linear combinations $(x_1, x_2) = x_1\vec{e}_1 + x_2\vec{e}_2$ are transformed into $x_1 Q\vec{e}_1 + x_2 Q\vec{e}_2$, i.e. are rotated likewise.

Define the transformation S by the formula:

$$\vec{x} = (x_1, x_2) \mapsto S\vec{x} = (x_1, -x_2).$$

It is the **reflection** about the line $x_2 = 0$ as the axis of symmetry. Obviously, S also preserves inner products and is therefore an isometry.

For any real number t, define the **translation** T by the vector $\vec{t} = (t, 0)$ as follows:

$$\vec{x} = (x_1, x_2) \mapsto T\vec{x} = (x_1 + t, x_2).$$

It is an isometry, because $|T\vec{x} - T\vec{y}| = |(\vec{x} + \vec{t}) - (\vec{y} + \vec{t})| = |\vec{x} - \vec{y}|$.

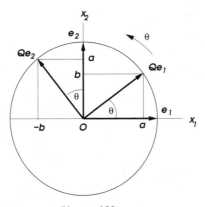

Figure 159

Using compositions of the transformations Q, S, and T, we can obtain translations by arbitrary vectors, rotations about arbitrary centers, and reflections about arbitrary lines (not necessarily passing through the origin). For instance, the translation by a vector $(-t, 0)$ moves the point with the radius-vector $(t, 0)$ to the origin. Applying then the rotation through an angle θ about the origin, followed by the translation by the vector $(t, 0)$, we obtain a rotation through the same angle θ about the translated center $(t, 0)$.

149. Theorem. *Every isometry of the Euclidean plane can be obtained by composing translations, rotations and reflections.*

We call X a **fixed point** of a geometric transformation F if $F(X) = X$.

Lemma. *An isometry of the Euclidean plane that has three non-collinear fixed points is the identity transformation.*

Let us assume that a given isometry F is not the identity. Then there exists a point Y such that $F(Y) \neq Y$. Then every point X fixed by the isometry F must be equidistant from Y and $F(Y)$, i.e. lie on the perpendicular bisector to the segment connecting Y and $F(Y)$. This contradicts the assumption that the three fixed points of F are non-collinear. Thus F is the identity.

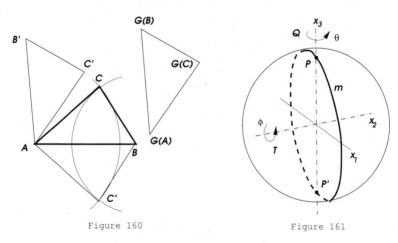

Figure 160   Figure 161

To prove the theorem, consider now an arbitrary isometry G of the plane, and pick any three non-collinear points A, B, and C (Figure 160). There exists a translation T that moves the point $G(A)$ back to A. Let B' and C' be obtained by applying T to $G(B)$ and $G(C)$ respectively. There exists a rotation Q about the center A that moves the ray AB' to AB. Moreover since G, T, and Q are isometries, the point $Q(B')$ coincides with B since both lie on the ray AB and are the same distance away from A. Let C'' denote the point $Q(C')$. Then C and C'' are equidistant from each of the points A and B, i.e. C and C'' are intersection points of two circles, one centered at A, the other at B. Since two circles intersect at two points symmetric about the line of centers, we conclude that either C and C'' coincide, or are symmetric about the line AB. In the 2nd case, the point C'' is moved to C by the transformation of reflection S about the line AB. Thus, the composition of G with the translation T, rotation Q, and (in the 2nd case) the reflection S, moves the points A, B, and C back to their original positions. By the lemma, the entire composition is the identity transformation. Undoing the transformations T, R (and in the 2nd case S) in the reverse order, i.e. applying R^{-1} followed by T^{-1} (in the 2nd case: S^{-1}, then R^{-1}, and then T^{-1}), we obtain a composition of translations, rotations, and possibly reflections which moves every point X to $G(X)$. Thus the isometry G is such a composition.

Remark. In fact every isometry of the Euclidean plane *is* the rotation through some angle about some center, reflection about some line, or translation by some vector.

150. Spherical geometry. Consider now the sphere of radius R, centered at the origin of the Euclidean space $\mathbf{R}^3$ which is equipped with the standard inner product:

$$(x_1, x_2, x_3) \cdot (y_1, y_2, y_3) = x_1 y_1 + x_2 y_2 + x_3 y_3.$$

Let P and P' (Figure 161) be the intersection points of the sphere with the x_3-axis, and m be the great circle, obtained by intersecting the sphere with the plane $x_2 = 0$. Define the rotation Q through the angle θ about the axis PP' by the formula:

$$\vec{x} = (x_1, x_2, x_3) \mapsto Q\vec{x} = (ax_1 - bx_2, bx_1 + ax_2, x_3),$$

where $a = \cos\theta$ and $b = \sin\theta$ satisfy $a^2 + b^2 = 1$. Define the **reflection** S about the great circle m as:

$$\vec{x} = (x_1, x_2, x_3) \mapsto S\vec{x} = (x_1, -x_2, x_3).$$

Define the rotation T through the angle ϕ about the x_2-axis as:

$$\vec{x} = (x_1, x_2, x_3) \mapsto T\vec{x} = (tx_1 - ux_3, x_2, ux_1 + tx_3),$$

where $t = \cos\phi$ and $u = \sin\phi$ satisfy $t^2 + u^2 = 1$.

The transformation Q preserves the inner product in $\mathbf{R}^3$ (i.e. $Q\vec{x} \cdot Q\vec{y} = \vec{x} \cdot \vec{y}$ for all vectors $\vec{x}, \vec{y}$), and the same holds true for S and T. In particular, Q, S, and T preserve the sphere, transform great circles to great circles, and preserve arc lengths. Composing these transformations, we obtain rotations of the sphere about arbitrary axes, and reflections about arbitrary great circles. All such transformations transform points $\pm\vec{x}$ centrally symmetric to each other

to centrally symmetric points. Therefore these transformations act
on the projective plane, and thus define isometries of the spherical
model of non-Euclidean plane geometry.

We leave it as an exercise to prove that *every isometry of the
sphere can be obtained as a composition of transformations Q, T, and
S.* In fact every isometry of the sphere *is* a rotation about an axis
or reflection about a great circle. However, when centrally symmetric points of the sphere are considered the same point, the reflection
(Y, Figure 162) of a point (X) about an equator (m) becomes indis-
tinguishable from the axial symmetry (i.e. rotation through $180°$)
about the diameter PP' connecting the corresponding poles. Therefore isometries of the spherical model of non-Euclidean geometry
reduce to rotations through arbitrary angles about arbitrary centers.

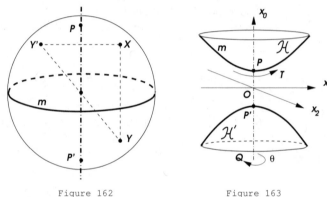

Figure 162   Figure 163

151. Hyperbolic geometry. In the space $\mathbf{R}^3$ equipped with
the Minkowski inner product

$$(x_0, x_1, x_2) \cdot (y_0, y_1, y_2) = -x_0y_0 + x_1y_1 + x_2y_2,$$

let $\mathcal{H}$ and $\mathcal{H}'$ be the two branches of the hyperboloid of revolution
given by the equation $x_0^2 - x_1^2 - x_2^2 = R^2$, P and P' (Figure 163) be
their intersection points with the x_0-axis, and m be the generatrix
of $\mathcal{H}$ obtained as the intersection with the plane $x_2 = 0$.

The transformation Q given by the formula

$$\vec{x} = (x_0, x_1, x_2) \mapsto Q\vec{x} = (x_0, ax_1 - bx_2, bx_1 + ax_2),$$

where $a = \cos\theta$, $b = \sin\theta$, defines in the Minkowski space the
rotation through the angle θ about the axis PP'. Define the reflection
S about the plane $x_2 = 0$ as:

$$\vec{x} = (x_0, x_1, x_2) \mapsto S\vec{x} = (x_0, x_1, -x_2).$$

These transformations preserve the inner product in the Minkowski space, and since they also fix the point P, they preserve the branch $\mathcal{H}$ of the hyperboloid $-\vec{x} \cdot \vec{x} = R^2$, and define isometries on it. Composing these transformations, we obtain isometries of the hyperbolic plane $\mathcal{H}$ which fix the point P: rotations about P and reflections about lines passing through P.

Introduce now a **hyperbolic rotation** T of the Minkowski space about the x_2-axis by the formula:

$$\vec{x} = (x_0, x_1, x_2) \mapsto T\vec{x} = (tx_0 + ux_1, ux_0 + tx_1, x_2),$$

where t and u are arbitrary real numbers satisfying $t^2 - u^2 = 1$. The hyperbolic rotation preserves inner products:

$$
\begin{aligned}
T\vec{x} \cdot T\vec{y} &= -(tx_0 + ux_1)(ty_0 + uy_1) + (ux_0 + tx_1)(uy_0 + ty_1) + x_2 y_2 \\
&= (u^2 - t^2)x_0 y_0 + (ut - tu)(x_0 y_1 - x_1 y_0) + (t^2 - u^2)x_1 y_1 + x_2 y_2 \\
&= -x_0 y_0 + x_1 y_1 + x_2 y_2 = \vec{x} \cdot \vec{y}.
\end{aligned}
$$

We have: $T(R, 0, 0) = (tR, uR, 0)$. Hence, if we require $t > 0$, the point $P = (R, 0, 0)$ is transformed into a point on the generatrix m of the same branch $\mathcal{H}$ of the hyperboloid. Then the whole branch $\mathcal{H}$ is preserved by T, which therefore defines an isometry of the hyperbolic plane. The point P can be moved by T to any point on the line m, and then to any point on the hyperbolic plane (by applying also rotations Q). Thus we have proved the following result (to be compared with Book I, §3).

152. Theorem. *For each of the three types of plane geometries (Euclidean, spherical, and hyperbolic), one can superimpose the plane onto itself* (using compositions of transformations Q and T) *in a way that moves any given point into any other given point, and any line through the first given point into any other given line through the second given point, and this can also be done after flipping the plane upside down* (by S).

Corollaries. (1) The plane $x_0 = R$ in the Minkowski space is orthogonal to the radius-vector $(R, 0, 0)$ of the point P. The plane intersects $\mathcal{H}$ only at the point P and is therefore tangent to $\mathcal{H}$ at P. Applying to this plane a composition of transformations Q, S, T which moves the point P into any other given point X on the hyperboloid, we obtain a plane tangent to $\mathcal{H}$ at X. Since the transformations preserve inner products in the Minkowski space, we conclude that *tangent planes to the hyperboloid are orthogonal to the radius-vectors of the tangency points.*

(2) The transformation T on the hyperbolic plane moves the point P to another point $P_1 = TP$ of the line m (Figure 164), and thus the whole line segment PP_1 to the line segment P_1P_2 of the same line m, where $P_2 = TP_1$. Applying T to P_1P_2 we obtain yet another segment P_2P_3 where $P_3 = TP_2$ is another point down the line m, and so on. Since T is an isometry, all the segments PP_1, P_1P_2, P_2P_3, etc. are congruent on the hyperbolic plane. We conclude that *on the hyperbolic plane, one can mark line segments of arbitrary length.*

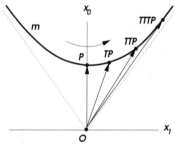

Figure 164

153. Remarks. (1) In hyperbolic geometry, too, each isometry can be obtained (see Exercises) by composing transformations Q, T and S of the hyperbolic plane. However the explicit description of all isometries looks slightly more complex than in the spherical or Euclidean case. Namely, beside reflections about arbitrary lines, there are three kinds of rotations, all induced by transformations of the Minkowski space preserving $\mathcal{H}$: **elliptic** rotations (e.g. Q) about a time-like axis, **hyperbolic** rotations (e.g. T) about a space-like axis, and **parabolic** rotations about a light-like axis.

(2) In each of the three models of plane geometry, the shortest paths between points are line segments. This allows one to characterize lines in terms of distances, and explains why isometries, which are defined as geometric transformations preserving distances, also happen to transform lines into lines.

(3) According to an idea of the German mathematician **Bernhard Riemann**, there exist models of (say, plane) geometry much more general than those the types discussed here. E.g. one can take any surface in space for the set of points, and shortest (inside the surface!) paths between points in the role of lines. It turns out however, that the three types of geometries: Euclidean, spherical, and hyperbolic, are singled out among more general **Riemann surfaces** as the only ones possessing enough isometries for the theorem of §152 to hold.

(4) Similarity transformations, i.e. geometric transformations preserving angles but changing the scale (and respectively figures which are similar but non-congruent) exist in Euclidean geometry but not in the spherical or hyperbolic one. That is, in non-Euclidean geometry, keeping all angles but changing the scale by a factor of k produces a new model, which cannot be identified with the original one by an isometry. To see this, apply in the Euclidean space $\mathbf{R}^3$ (in the spherical case) or in the Minkowski space $\mathbf{R}^3$ (in the hyperbolic case), the homothety with the coefficient $k > 0$ with respect to the center O. This homothety transforms the sphere of radius R into the sphere of radius kR, and the hyperboloid $-\vec{x} \cdot \vec{x} = R^2$ into the one given by the equation $-\vec{x} \cdot \vec{x} = k^2 R^2$. However the spheres or hyperboloids corresponding to different values of R cannot be identified by isometries. Indeed, as it follows from §144 and §146, the area of a spherical or hyperbolic triangle with given angles depends on R.

(5) One can develop spherical and hyperboloid models of *solid* non-Euclidean geometry by starting with the Euclidean or Minkowski inner product in $\mathbf{R}^4$.

EXERCISES

306. What isometry of the Euclidean plane can result from composing: (a) two reflections; (b) two rotations?

307. Find the geometric locus of points in the spherical model of non-Euclidean geometry equidistant from: (a) a point; (b) a line.

308.[*] Find all triples of whole numbers $p \geq q \geq r \geq 2$ such that the triangle with the angles $2d/p$, $2d/q$, and $2d/r$ lies on the sphere. Show that reflections in the sides of such a triangle, and their compositions form a finite set of isometries of the sphere.
Hint: Compare with symmetries of suitable polyhedra.

309. Let $t > 0$ and u be real numbers such that $t^2 - u^2 = 1$, and let T and T' be the hyperbolic rotations about the x_2-axis (Figure 163) corresponding to the pairs (t, u) and $(t, -u)$. Prove that $T' = T^{-1}$.

310. Prove that vectors tangent to the hyperbolic plane $\mathcal{H}$ in the Minkowski space are space-like.
Hint: Verify this when the point of tangency is P (Figure 163), and apply isometries.

311. Prove that the cross section of the hyperbolic plane $\mathcal{H}$ by a plane in the Minkowski space, parallel to the tangent plane of $\mathcal{H}$ at a given point, is a **circle** centered at the given point, i.e. consists of all points equidistant from it in hyperbolic geometry.

312. Prove that on the hyperbolic plane $\mathcal{H}$, the geometric locus of points equidistant from a given line is the cross section of $\mathcal{H}$ by a pair of parallel planes centrally symmetric about the origin.

313. Prove that every pair of points A and A' on the hyperbolic plane $\mathcal{H}$ is symmetric about the line, obtained as the intersection of $\mathcal{H}$ with the subspace of dimension 2 in the Minkowski space orthogonal to the vector $\overrightarrow{AA'}$, and that this line is the geometric locus of points equidistant from A and A'.

314. Prove that an isometry of the hyperbolic plane that fixes three non-collinear points is the identity, and derive from this that any isometry of the hyperbolic plane can be obtained by composing transformations Q, T, and S defined in §151.

*315.** Suppose that two lines on the hyperbolic plane are obtained by intersecting $\mathcal{H}$ with two subspaces of dimension 2 in the Minkowski space. Describe the result of composing reflections about these lines, if the intersection of the subspaces is: (a) time-like; (b) space-like; (c) light-like.

*316.** Prove that every isometry of the Euclidean or non-Euclidean plane can be composed of one, two, or three reflections.

*317.** Prove that on the Euclidean or non-Euclidean plane, a straight segment is the shortest path between its endpoints.

Hint: Show that every path connecting the same endpoints but avoiding any given point of the segment can be replaced with a shorter path passing through it.

Translator's Afterword

Three Controversies about

Mathematics, Geometry, and Education

What we think of mathematics, and how we teach and learn it (or not), determines to a large degree the place it takes in our culture. Regardless of what we think, mathematics enters our life by providing us with idealized models of real phenomena and showing us how to deal with them logically and creatively. At the end of a traditional course in elementary geometry, a subject seen for centuries as the essence of mathematics, it is tempting to examine whether what we think of it is true. Here is a brief summary of the three (most influential in my opinion) **common views** of mathematics, and of geometry in particular:

   * Mathematics is a relative wisdom; mathematical theorems, being logical consequences of axioms, are representative of real world relationships only to the degree that the axioms are.

   ** A key virtue of mathematics (as well as the notorious difficulty of it) resides in the strict deductive nature of mathematical reasoning, as is best demonstrated by elementary Euclidean geometry.

   *** To offset the difficulty and provide for success in education, early exposure to elements of Euclidean geometry is highly recommended.

Usually such views are conveyed to the broad educated audience via the high-school geometry course, but they sound self-explanatory and uncontroversial anyway, and are readily endorsed by those who are professionally affiliated with mathematical education.

In these notes, we will see, drawing some examples from the main text of this book, that these views are essentially **misleading**, as they are either outdated or a result of terminological confusion and mis-information about the history and essence of mathematics, and that the direction in education suggested by them is rather perverted.

*

It is true that classical elementary geometry was developed by postulating basic properties of space in the form of *axioms*, and logically deriving further properties from them. It is also true that modern mathematics often relies on the *axiomatic method*. It turns out however that what is meant by *axioms* has changed. Nowadays, axioms are used for unification purposes, i.e. in order to study several similar examples at once. For instance (§140), *symmetricity* and *bilinearity* are axioms defining an *inner product*, a notion that unifies the *Euclidean* (§140) and *Minkowski* (§145) dot products. Another example: the eight axioms of a *vector space* (§137) unify coordinate vectors (§142) with geometric ones (§119).

Studying properties of several similar objects at once is a very common method, and one sure way by which mathematics *saves effort* (using an expression of Ron Aharoni [15]) and thus becomes useful. Axioms here are simply part of a definition, i.e. a *convention* which calls an object by such-and-such a name if it possesses the required properties; in mathematics they are not "self-evident truths accepted without proof," as the conventional wisdom would have it. For instance, the definition of *regular polyhedra* in §84 is *axiomatic*, as opposed to the *constructive* description of the five Platonic solids given in §§85–86. The theorem of §87 illustrates the use of the axiomatic method for purposes of *classification* (of regular polyhedra, in this example). Similar applications are found in §142 ("uniqueness" of Euclidean geometry) and §§149–151 (characterization of isometries).

It often happens that general results and concepts of mathematics, initially motivated by known examples, are successfully applied in unexpected ways to new situations. The alternative scenario: an axiomatic theory developed with *no* examples known to satisfy the axioms, is rather unusual. Thus mathematics appears today not as a "relative wisdom" (where conclusions hold *if* the axioms are satisfied) but as a *science* motivated by studying important and interesting examples, for which the conclusions *do* hold because the axioms *are* satisfied. Such examples often come as mathematical models of real phenomena. The most basic of these models deal with comparing finite sets of objects, and the correct way of manipulating them is not decided by any system of axioms. It is learned (even by advanced mathematicians) through the tedious process of *counting* — in childhood.

Then what about classical Euclidean geometry? The way it was developed seems today quite similar to some advanced branches of theoretical physics, notably *string theory*. Sometimes physics goes beyond of what is known in mathematics and needs mathematical models that are not available. Then physicists use *heuristic* methods: they *postulate* the existence of certain models with certain properties, and prescribe certain rules of manipulating them, even though there is not a single example that fits the description. This is similar to how *non-Euclidean geometry* first emerged in the work of Lobachevsky and Bolyai (§134). Later, if physicists' expectations turn out to be reasonable, mathematicians construct the required models, such as the hyperbolic (§146) and projective (§144) planes in the case of non-Euclidean geometry. But until then, heuristic methods prevail in describing physical reality.

This is how *space* is described in classical Euclidean geometry, both in antiquity (see §133) and in modern age (Book I, §§1–5). One would examine the images of a stretched thread, a light ray, or the surface of a pond or desk, introduce *infinitesimally* thin and *infinitely* spread idealizations of these objects, postulate those properties of lines and planes which appear obvious from the heuristic point of view, and then obtain further properties by reasoning. The reader can check that this was the way the foundations of geometry were treated by Euclid [1]. The physicists' heuristic approach to the foundations of elementary geometry worked well for mankind for over two millennia. This approach should suffice even today for anyone studying the subject for the first time.

* *

According to the author of a modern Russian textbook [9], "Geometry is a subject for those who like to dream, draw and examine pictures, and who are good at making observations and drawing conclusions." According to an expert at a homeschool math blog popular in the U.S., "high school geometry with its formal (two-column) proofs is considered hard and detached from practical life." Sounds different? How come?

This time, it is *geometry* that means two different things. In various countries, at different periods, the same new current in math education emerged. The main idea was to bring high-school mathematics to a level contemporary to the 20th century. In geometry, it meant introducing set-theoretic terminology and emphasizing the role of geometric transformations. In Russia, *Kolmogorov's reform* took place in late seventies, and was immediately recognized as a failure (which seems to be the fate — for a variety of causes — of all reforms in education). It did affect the quality of instruction, but it shook only slightly the status of geometry as the most inspiring part of the math curriculum. The analogous reform in the U.S., which took place in the sixties and was dubbed *New Math*, was accompanied also with the intention of introducing mathematics "the correct way" right from the start (as opposed to raising the level of abstraction in stages). For geometry this meant: to erect it on a rigorous axiomatic foundation.

The search for a solid foundation for geometry has played an important role in the development of mathematics (see §134). As was mentioned in the previous section, this problem emerges not in a first study of the subject, but later, when the building is already there and the question of what it stands on remains. Modern mathematics solves this problem by introducing geometry through vector algebra (as it is done in §§136–141). The vector approach is considered "the royal road to geometry": it is logically simple, and intuitively transparent, since vectors come from physics. It also brings into elementary geometry new problems and methods (see §§119–132), and paves the road to more advanced mathematics, such as *linear algebra*.

The New Math reform attempted to bring rigor into a beginner's course of elementary geometry by following, albeit loosely, Hilbert's axiomatic approach (§135). Apparently, Hilbert's monograph [2] was misconstrued as a contemporary exposition of elementary geometry. In fact this work played a key role in forming another branch of mathematics, *mathematical logic*, but added little to classical geometry and nothing to modern. Moreover, according to a leading French mathematician David Ruelle [12], "Hilbert's version of Euclidean geometry without the help of (1) [visual experience and intuition] and (2) [drawings] shows how hard the subject really is."

The focus of the post-New Math geometry courses falls, therefore, on deductive reasoning, understood as the task of meticulous conversion of hypotheses into conclusions. The format of *two-column proofs* is implemented to streamline the process (see an example in §137): the left column is for *what* is claimed, and the right for *why*. In the genre of two-column proofs, it takes several lines to fully justify even an obvious statement (e.g. that if one angle formed by two intersecting lines is right then the other three angles they form are also right). Instead of shortcutting to deep and beautiful geometric results, these textbooks either cast these results away or render them in fine print, and dedicate whole chapters to *formal proofs* of *trivial*, i.e. relatively obvious, facts.

In real mathematics, ancient or modern, there is no such thing as "two-column" proofs (as opposed to "paragraph" ones), just as there is no division of proofs into "formal" and "informal." What, indeed, is a proof? In science, we want to know not only *what* is true but also *why* it is so, and a proof is an answer to the latter question. There is a subtlety though.

In mathematics, we systematically use the advantage of building new knowledge upon previously established facts (and this is yet another way that mathematics saves effort). It is not prohibited even in math to use heuristic, plausible reasoning. For instance, one can form many composite numbers by multiplying a few primes, and so it seems *plausible* that prime numbers should occur sparsely among all whole numbers. While there exist mathematical theorems that make this intuition precise, the statement taken too literally is expected to be false: according to the famous *twin prime conjecture*, there are infinitely many pairs of primes that are only 2 units apart, like 29 and 31, or 41 and 43. Clearly, deriving logical conclusions from observations that are only roughly correct and admit exceptions, may lead to false results and contradictions. What is even worse, according to the rules of logic, a proposition *"A implies B"* is true when A is false. Hence, a single contradiction would rob one of the very means to obtain reliable conclusions by logic: if *some A* were both true and false, then so would *every B*! The method of building towers of new conclusions upon previously established facts requires, therefore, that mathematical propositions be stated in a form that would *allow no exceptions whatsoever*. Thus, the answer to the question of *why* such a proposition is true should also explain why it allows no exceptions whatsoever. Whenever an argument is neat enough to be convincing in this regard, it qualifies as a mathematical proof.

Those who manage to evade the burden of two-column proofs and succeed in studying elementary geometry know firsthand that mathematics can be valuable or difficult not due to the neat reasoning involved (which does come in handy at times), but because mathematical gems reveal themselves only when insight and ingenuity come into play.

* *
*

To repair the damage made by the increasingly formal style and shallow content of high-school geometry courses, two remedies were invented.

The first one (apparently implemented in most U.S. high-schools) was to abandon the whole subject of classical elementary geometry in favor of elements of analytical geometry and coordinate linear algebra. This approach to geometry (see §§209–212 of Book I and §§142, 148 of Book II) is well suited for developing routine exercises and algorithmic techniques. A typical result for geometry instruction of this type is the ultimate loss of the features, such as challenge and originality, that mark good science.

In the other approach, one intends to keep elementary geometry in school (however formal and shallow, or even if only as an *honors* course) by offering a preliminary, preparatory course of *informal* geometry (as opposed to *rigorous* one). While in some cases this becomes simply the return to a traditional geometry course (similar to Book I), more often this means: rendering math by examples, and "without proof," i.e. dogmatically. As a variation, some popular textbooks of rigorous geometry realize the same idea by exposing the reader to "formal proofs" only *after* introducing many geometric facts in a series of chapters written "informally." Both variations fit a more general philosophy, according to which a high level of intellectual maturity is required to succeed in studying classical Euclidean geometry, and to reach this level, gradual exposure to geometric ideas is proposed. Many modern math curricula adopt this philosophy and dedicate to geometry substantial portions of study time in middle and even elementary school. As we noted earlier, these ideas sound quite reasonable, so it is worth taking a look at where they lead.

It is important to realize that mathematics per se (as opposed to the way it is taught) is not inherently evil, and so if it avoids using some simple methods, there usually are reasons for this. For example, it is not hard to measure the sum of the angles of a triangle and find that it is about 180°. What is not possible to do by such measuring is to figure out why all triangles have the same sum of the angles, for one thing, because there are infinitely many triangles, and for another, because that is actually false (see §144) for triangles on the surface of the globe. Approaching geometry informally (i.e. neglecting logical relations) makes it hard to determine what is true and why. In geometry education, this usually leads to the dogmatic style, and (what is even worse) mathematical *knowledge* being systematically replaced with *tautology*. To illustrate the latter point, we discuss here three exercises taken from the chapter *Geometric figures* in a popular pre-algebra textbook [13].

(1) *Classify each given triangle by its* (given) *angles*. To "classify" means to decide if the triangle is acute, right or obtuse. One should realize that triangles are not inherently divided into acute, right or obtuse, but it is people who *agreed* to classify triangles this way. They did so in order to express geometric knowledge, e.g. to answer the question: *Does the orthocenter of a given triangle lie inside or outside it?* The answer is *inside* for acute and *outside* for obtuse triangles. But the mere question about classifying the triangles by angles is *tautological*, as an answer would contain no geometric information beyond what is directly given.

(2) *Find the measure of each angle of a regular pentagon, **given that** the sum of the measures of the angles of a pentagon is* 540°. A totally blind space alien who has no idea what polygons, angles or degrees are,

will successfully answer this question if told that *by the very definition* a regular pentagon has five angles of equal measure: 540° divided by 5 is equal to 108°. Not only does this exercise require no information beyond a definition, but it does not even require any visual interpretation of the definition. The same answer would involve non-tautological reasoning, if the sum of the angles were not given.

(3) *Find the perimeter of each polygon* (with the lengths of the sides labeled on a diagram). The *perimeter*, defined as the distance around a figure, is a favorite geometry topic of many elementary school curricula. In fact this definition is merely an English translation of the Greek word *perimeter*. A kindergartener, asked to find the length of the fence around a lot with five sides of $1, 2, 3, 4$, and 10 yards long, will be able to answer: $1 + 2 + 3 + 4 + 10 = 20$ yards. Thus the difficulty of the whole topic is purely linguistic, namely in the use of a foreign word. To emphasize that solving such exercises is void of any geometric content, I chose unrealistic numbers: the pentagon, whose perimeter of 20 yards has just been successfully computed, cannot exist because of the triangle inequality (Book I, §49).

Of course, conventions such as definitions and notations are present in every mathematical text, since they are needed for expressing mathematical knowledge. Unfortunately, geometric portions of typical elementary school curricula are dedicated entirely to conventions and tautologies. This is not just a result of poor realization of good intentions, since it comes framed as a certain ideology. Known as *the van Hiele model*, this ideology merits a brief description.

According to the van Hiele model, the ability of a learner to process geometric knowledge is determined by the *level* of geometric abstraction achieved by this learner. At level 0, one is only able to identify geometric shapes (e.g.: this is a rectangle). At level 1, one is able to attribute properties to shapes (e.g.: a rectangle has four right angles, and two diagonals of the same length). At level 2, one becomes capable of deriving relationships between the properties (e.g.: *if* the four angles of a quadrilateral are right, *then* it must be a rectangle, and *hence* its diagonals have the same length). At level 3, one is able to appreciate an entire logical theory that tracks all properties of geometric shapes back to axioms. At level 4, one can freely navigate through and compare abstract axiomatic theories (such as non-Euclidean geometries) not relying on geometric intuition. The main point of the model is that, regardless of age, a learner cannot progress to the next level until he is firmly grounded in the previous one.

In the half century since its invention, this classification of five levels has been the subject and the basis of many projects in education, and is considered a well-established classical theory. It is quite remarkable, therefore, that at a closer look the theory itself turns out to be *almost entirely a tautology*. For comparison, imagine a "theory" claiming that high-school students are divided into three categories: those who carry less than \$20 in their pockets, those who carry from \$20 to \$100, and those who carry over \$100. One can develop a field study on a school's campus and confirm that "the theory works!" In application to van Hiele's levels, such a field study has been conducted, and the results reported in the book [14]. The fact that the classification into van Hiele's levels, however smart and elegant, is merely a *definition*, and so it cannot be confirmed or disproved by any experiments, seems to escape, somehow, the researchers' attention.

The part of the van Hiele model that can be true or false (and hence is capable of carrying knowledge) consists of the claims that *a learner of geometry cannot reach the next level while bypassing the previous one.* These are four essentially independent claims (about reaching levels 1,2,3, and 4). In fact the last two are true *tautologically*, simply because *many* is more than *one*. Indeed, operating with axiomatic theories (level 4) includes operating with one of them (level 3). Likewise, deriving *all* properties of geometric figures from axioms (level 3) includes deriving *some* properties from others (level 2). What remains are the assumptions that before attempting a rigorous geometry course one has to go through two preliminary stages: first becoming familiar with basic geometric shapes, and then learning to discern their mathematical properties intuitively. These assumptions are used to justify the ways geometry is presented throughout elementary and middle school, and so they are important.

A beginner's experience with geometric shapes should not be taken lightly, since it is one of two primary places where mathematics meets the real world (the other one being *counting*). All basic notions of geometry are somehow abstracted from this experience. The trouble is that the experience is often confused with the skill of naming shapes correctly: "this is a triangle, and this is a square." Educational psychologists illustrate a typical "difficulty" with this example: a beginner would not recognize a *square* as a (special case of) *rectangle*, but would classify it as a distinct shape. In fact the beginner is right: a square is a special case of rectangle not *intrinsically*, but only *by convention*, while by another convention (see Book I, §96) a parallelogram is *not* considered a special case of trapezoid. A convention is not something one can *figure out*. In mathematics, giving names to objects is the function of *definitions*, not *theorems*. Likewise, in real life, focusing on how things are called is void of any knowledge about them, and is in this sense *meaningless*. Here are some examples of *meaningful* questions.

1. Why are doors and windows rectangular and not triangular? (To understand why, imagine how a triangular board with hinges would open.) This question focuses on the properties of objects as determined by their shapes, whatever the names might be.

2. Why are sewer hole covers often shaped as disks but rarely as squares? The conventional answer to this question says that a square, turned sideways in space, can fall into the hole it covers, but a disk cannot. This may bring up another question: *Are disks the only shapes with this property?*

3. How would a car move if the wheels were shaped as (regular) pentagons, or hexagons? Well, it would not move very smoothly. The wheels are mounted to the car's axes by their centers, and what matters is that the distance from the center to boundary points of the pentagon (or hexagon) varies. This question leads directly to the definition of a circle as the locus of points on the plane *equidistant* from the center.

4. A traditional technique of relocating buildings consists in placing round wood trunks of the same diameter under a (raised) house and rolling it to a new place. *Would the technique work well if the trunks had square cross sections?* In fact, what matters here is that a disk has the same *width* in every direction, and the square does not. *Are there figures of constant width other than disks?*

Generally speaking, it is not easy to invent geometry questions that are meaningful yet elementary. What helps *understanding* (as opposed to merely *naming*) geometric shapes is not classroom discussions but the fact that shapes around us do matter. One learns what a right angle is by fitting a bookshelf and a sofa bed next to each other, and encounters parallelograms and trapezoids by drawing buildings according to the rules of perspective.

Finally, let us return to the idea that an informal approach to geometry must precede the rigorous one. On the one hand, the statement sounds self-defying. If one cannot begin with the rigorous approach, then, since this is a relatively new pedagogical theory, how did people manage to learn Euclidean geometry in the previous two millennia? On the other hand, it seems obvious indeed, that Euclidean geometry is demanding of the learner's intellectual maturity, including the ability to concentrate, think, reason, meet a challenge, read a book focusing on every detail, use concise expression and precise terminology, etc.

The solution to this dilemma is very simple. The subject of Euclidean geometry does not lend itself to purely intuitive, non-rigorous treatment. It begins where Euclid began: from describing basic properties of abstract points, lines, planes, and using imagination and logic in order to discover and prove properties of geometric figures. To prepare oneself to study geometry, anything that requires imagination and logic, *apart from geometry itself*, is suitable. Mathematics of the elementary school becomes one such area, if studied not dogmatically but with full understanding of *why* it works. Meaningful geometric content is very limited there, but in basic arithmetic, one needs to go through many deep and subtle mathematical ideas in order to fully appreciate the decimal number system, standard algorithms, and operations with fractions (see [15]). To mention more: natural sciences (e.g. the structure of electron shells in atoms, the periodic table of chemical elements and genetics); computers and programming languages (e.g. the robotic system *LEGO Mindstorm*); the grammar of natural languages; music and the theory of harmony; visual arts (e.g. origami); games and puzzles (e.g. chess or the Rubik's Cube). Anything real, which is not a tautology but is rich with genuine, deep, non-trivial knowledge and structure, prepares one for studying geometry and more advanced mathematics. Everything fake: a substitute invented to facilitate instruction (be it *Informal Geometry* or even *Calculus*), has the opposite effect.

Bibliography

[1] Euclid. *The Thirteen Books of the Elements.* Translated with introduction and commentary by T. L. Heath. Vol. 1 (Books I–II), vol. 2 (Books III–IX), vol. 3 (Books X–XIII): Dover, New York, 1956.

[2] David Hilbert, *The Foundations of Geometry.* Authorized translation by E. J. Townsend. The Open Court, La Salle, Illinois, 1950.

[3] Reviel Netz. *The Shaping of Deduction in Greek Mathematics: A Study in Cognitive History.* Cambridge University Press, 1999.

[4] A. P. Kiselev. *Kiselev's Geometry. Book I, Planimetry.* Adapted from Russian by Alexander Givental. Sumizdat, El Cerrito, 2006.

Editions of Kiselev's *Geometry* the translation is based on:

[5] A. P. Kiselev. *Elementary Geometry, for Secondary Educational Institutions.* Part I: *Planimetry.* Part II. *Stereometry.* First edition: Dumnov's Bookstore, Moscow, 1892.

[6] A. P. Kiselev. *Elementary Geometry.* Prosveshchenie, Moscow, 1980, 1998.

Some ideas for additional exercises were borrowed from:

[7] V. B. Lidsky et al. *Problems in Elementary Mathematics.* Nauka, Moscow, 1967 (in Russian).

[8] V. V. Prasolov. *Problems on planimetry.* Part 2. Nauka, Moscow, 1991 (in Russian).

[9] I. F. Sharygin. *Geometry. Grades 10–11.* Drofa, Moscow, 2007; *Geometry. Stereometry. Problems.* Drofa, Moscow, 2000; *Geometry. Planimetry. Problems. Grades 9–11.* Drofa, Moscow, 2001 (in Russian).

[10] I. H. Sivashinsky. *Problems in Elementary Mathematics.* Nauka, Moscow, 1966 (in Russian).

[11] M. I. Skanavi (editor) *Collected Mathematics Problems for Technical College Applicants.* Vysshaya Shkola, Moscow, 1988 (in Russian).

Sources quoted in the Afterword:

[12] David Ruelle. *Conversations on mathematics with a visitor from outer space.* http://www.ihes.fr/~ruelle/PUBLICATIONS/126imu.ps.

[13] M. Dolciani, R. Sorgenfrey, J. Graham. *Pre-algebra. An accelerated course.* Houghton–Mifflin Co., Boston, 1989.

[14] D. Fuys, D. Geddes, R. Tischler. *The van Hiele model of thinking in geometry among adolescents.* Journal for Research in Mathematics Education. Monograph No. 3, NCTM, 1988.

[15] R. Aharoni. *Arithmetic for parents. A book for grownups about children's mathematics.* Sumizdat, El Cerrito, 2007.

Index